8TH
BLUE BOOK
DOLLS & VALUES®

by Jan Foulke
photographs by Howard Foulke

Published by   Hobby House Press, Inc.
Cumberland, Maryland 21502

Other Titles by Author:

Blue Book of Dolls & Values®
2nd Blue Book of Dolls & Values®
3rd Blue Book of Dolls & Values®
4th Blue Book of Dolls & Values®
5th Blue Book of Dolls & Values®
6th Blue Book of Dolls & Values®
7th Blue Book of Dolls & Values®
Focusing on Effanbee Composition Dolls
Focusing on Treasury of Mme. Alexander Dolls
Focusing on Gebrüder Heubach Dolls
Kestner: King of Dollmakers
Simon & Halbig Dolls: The Artful Aspect
Doll Classics

The doll prices given within this book are intended as value guides rather than arbitrarily set prices. Each doll price recorded here is actually a compilation. The retail prices in this book are recorded as accurately as possible but in the case of errors, typographical, clerical or otherwise, the author and publisher assume no liability nor responsibility for any loss incurred by users of this book.

FRONT COVER: *Triste* or long face Jumeau. See pages 116 and 244 for further information.

TITLE PAGE: 24in (61cm) closed-mouth Kestner. *Betty Harms Collection.*

ADDITIONAL COPIES AVAILABLE @ $14.95 PLUS $1.75 POSTAGE FROM
HOBBY HOUSE PRESS, INC.
900 FREDERICK STREET
CUMBERLAND, MARYLAND 21502

ISBN: 0-87588-317-6

Using This Book

Doll collecting is increasing in popularity every year. This large group of collectors entering the field has prompted more and larger doll shows, more dealers in dolls, more books on dolls, thicker doll magazines, and more doll conventions and seminars, as well as an overwhelming offering of new dolls by mass-production companies and individual artists. The most significant affect this great expansion has on the doll market concerns the increased demand for old dolls as more collectors are vying for the same number of dolls.

With the average old doll representing a purchase of at least several hundred dollars, today's collectors must be as well-informed as possible about the dolls they are considering as additions to their collections.

Since the first *BLUE BOOK OF DOLLS & VALUES* published in 1974, our objectives have remained the same:

• To present a book which will help collectors to identify dolls and learn more about them.

• To provide retail prices as a guide for buyers and sellers of dolls.

Since every edition of the *BLUE BOOK* has sold more than the previous one, we can only conclude that these objectives are in line with the needs of doll lovers, collectors, dealers and appraisers who keep buying the latest editions of our book.

The dolls presented in this book are listed alphabetically by the maker, material or the trade name of the individual doll. An extensive index has been provided to help in locating a specific doll. Of course, in a book this

16in (41cm) Lenci boy, 300 series, all original. *Esther Schwartz Collection.* (For more information see page 296.)

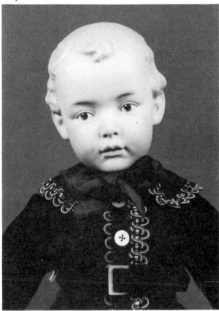

20in (51cm) Gebrüder Heubach 7622 character boy. *Esther Schwartz Collection.* (For more information see page 222.)

size, not every doll ever made can be discussed, but we have tried to include a broad spectrum of dolls which are available, desirable, interesting, popular and even some that are rare.

For each doll we have provided historical information, a description of the doll, a copy of the mark or label, the retail selling price and, in most cases, a photograph or a picture reference to a previous edition of the *BLUE BOOK* as there is not enough space to show a photograph of each doll in each edition. The historical information given for some of the dolls would have been much more difficult to compile were it not for the original research already published by Dorothy S., Elizabeth A. and Evelyn J. Coleman; Johana G. Anderton; and Jürgen and Marianne Cieslik.

The data of the retail prices was gathered from January to August 1987 from antique shops and shows, auctions, doll shops and shows, advertisements in collectors' periodicals, lists from doll dealers, and purchases and sales reported by both collectors and dealers. For price information on some of the rarer dolls, we had to dip back into 1986. The information was computed into the range of prices shown in this book. These prices are not merely our own valuations and judgments, although they must necessarily enter in; the prices are the results of our research as to the actual retail prices at which these dolls were either sold or offered for sale. If we could not find a sufficient number of dolls to be sure of giving a reliable range, we reported the information we could find and marked those prices "**."

In setting a price for each doll, we use a range to allow for the variables of originality, quality and condition which must reflect in the price. As collectors become more sophisticated in their purchases, fine examples of a doll, especially those which are all original or with period clothing, can bring a premium of up to 50% more than prices quoted for ordinary examples.

All prices given for antique dolls are for those of good quality and condition, but showing normal wear, and appropriately dressed in new or old clothing, unless other specifications are given in the description accompanying that particular doll. Bisque or china heads should not be cracked, broken or repaired, but may have slight making imperfections. Bodies may have repairs, but should be old and appropriate to the head. A doll with old dress, shoes and wig will generally be higher than quoted prices

23in (58cm) French Schmitt, beautiful contemporary wig and clothing. *Betty Harms Collection.* (For more information see page 353.)

as these items are in scarce supply and can easily cost over $50 each if purchased separately.

Prices given for modern dolls are for those in overall very good to excellent condition with original hair and clothing, except as noted. Composition may be slightly crazed, but should be colorful. Hard plastic and vinyl must be perfect. A never-played-with doll in original box with tagged clothing would bring a higher price than those quoted.

The users of this book must keep in mind that no price guide is the final word. It cannot provide the absolute answer of what to pay. It should be used only as an aid in purchasing a doll. The final decision must be yours, for only you are on the scene actually examining the specific doll in question. No book can take the place of actual field experience. Doll popularity can cycle; prices can fluctuate; regional variations can occur. Before you buy, do a lot of looking. Ask questions. Most dealers and collectors are glad to talk about their dolls and pleased to share their information with you.

It is interesting to note areas of price change in this edition from previous ones. The Bru bébés have become very popular again and are rising in price after quite a few years of simply remaining steady. The Jumeau bébés are up also, but not as much as the Brus. Since the identification of the smiling Bru lady doll, she has become very strong and is making her first appearance in the *BLUE BOOK.* The Jumeau lady doll has shown a great increase in price, especially in the large sizes. Other French fashion dolls are continuing to rise in price with early Huret dolls at the top.

American cloth dolls continue to be strong, a large increase showing in the W.P.A. Milwaukee model even though it is not an early doll. Wax dolls, particularly the English poured ones which are so realistic, have increased considerably in price, and this interest is spilling over into the better quality wax-over-composition as well as reinforced wax models.

Several types of dolls, long con-

6

sidered stepchildren by many collectors, at long last are gaining in popularity and price. Among these are the metal head dolls if they are in good condition with old bodies and clothing, the Sonneberg-type papier-mâché heads with molded hair, the medium quality wax-over dolls, and the "flattop" china heads, especially with old bodies and clothing. These are still reasonably priced in comparison with the German bisque dolls. It only stands to reason that budget-minded collectors would seek out less popular types of antique dolls at lower prices, but in so doing they are pushing up this market also.

Among newer dolls, there is increased interest and also a price rise in the celluloid dolls of all types, but particularly the German "Turtle Mark" dolls which are excellent quality.

The downward trend has continued with regard to the German closed-mouth dolls on kid bodies, but the early Kestner dolls with open mouth and square cut teeth are on the upswing.

Most of the Alexander dolls with vinyl heads, even the discontinued ones, still have not regained former popularity and price. New and current Alexander dolls are selling at auction for wholesale prices, rather than retail or above as previously.

Acknowledgements

Once again, I would like to thank all of our friends, associates, and readers in the doll world for their encouragement and cooperation in the preparation of this *8th BLUE BOOK OF DOLLS & VALUES.*

Those who allowed us to use photographs of their dolls or who provided special information for aspects of this edition were indispensable: Vivian C. Flagg, H&J Foulke, Inc., Virginia Ann Heyerdahl, Yvonne Baird, Joanna Ott, Richard Wright Antiques, Richard Saxman, Joan Tuck, Carolyn Guzzio, Richard W. Withington, Inc., Leone McMullen, Betty Harms, Dolly Valk, Esther Schwartz, Doodlebug Doll & Toy Shop, Kay & Wayne Jensen, Miriam Blankman, Hazel Scherf, Jackie Brown, Lana Norlin, Jane Alton, Elizabeth McIntyre, Joe Jackson & Joel Pearson, Wenham Museum, Wenham, MA, Anna May Case, Ruth Noden, Ralph Griffith, Jackie Kaner, Sandra Pipes, Carole Stoessel-Zvonar, Mary Lou Rubright, Sandy Coons, Maurine Popp, Lesley Hurford, Nancy Smith, Catherine Magann, Ann Dinnsen, Grace Dyar, India Stoessel, Mary Pat Houston, Joan Eickelberg, Roberta Roberts, Rosemary Dent, Beth Foulke, Carol Green, Betty Lunz — and those who wished their contribution to remain anonymous.

The Colemans who allowed some marks to be reproduced from their book, *The Collector's Encyclopedia of Dolls.*

Donna H. Felger, my editor, as well as the staff of Hobby House Press, Inc., who worked on this book.

Howard, for his beautiful photographs and for believing in me.

All of these people helped to make this *8th BLUE BOOK OF DOLLS & VALUES* a reality.

Investing in Dolls

With the price of the average old doll representing a purchase of at least several hundred dollars in today's doll market, the assembling of a doll collection becomes rather costly. Actually, very few people buy dolls strictly as an investment; most collectors buy a doll because they like it. It has appeal to them for some reason: perhaps as an object of artistic beauty, perhaps because it evokes some kind of sentiment, perhaps it fills some need that they feel or speaks to something inside them. It is this personal feeling toward the doll which makes it of value to the collector.

However, most collectors expect to at least break even when they eventually sell their dolls. Unfortunately, there is no guarantee that any particular doll will appreciate consistently year after year; however, the track record for old or antique dolls is fairly good. If you are thinking of the future sale of your collection, be wary of buying expensive new or reproduction dolls. They have no track record and little resale value.

Because most collectors have only limited funds for purchasing dolls, they must be sure they are spending their dollars to the best advantage. There are many factors to consider when buying a doll, and this chapter will give some suggestions about what to look for and what to consider. It follows also that if a collector is not particularly well-informed about the doll in question, he should not purchase it unless he has confidence in the person selling it to him.

MARKS

Fortunately for collectors most of

22in (56cm) poured wax child, all original. *Pearl D. Morley Collection.* (For more information see page 390.)

the antique bisque, some of the papier-mâché, cloth and other types of antique dolls are marked or labeled. The mark gives the buyer confidence: he or she knows exactly what has been purchased because of the mark or label which has given a trade name or identified the maker or the country of origin or even given a patent date or a style or mold number.

Most composition and modern dolls are marked with the maker's name and sometimes also the trade name of the doll and the date. Some dolls have tags sewn on or into their clothing to identify them; many still retain original hang tags.

Of course, many dolls are unmarked, but after you have seen quite

16in (41cm) Kestner 183 character boy. *Esther Schwartz Collection.* (For more information see page 262.)

a few dolls, you begin to notice their individual characteristics so that you can often determine what a doll possibly is. After a collector has some experience buying dolls, he or she begins to recognize an unusual face or an especially fine quality doll. Then there should be no hesitation about buying a doll marked only with a mold number or no mark at all. Many fine and unusual dolls do not carry a maker's name or any identifying number or symbol. The doll has to speak for itself, and the price must be based upon the collector's frame of doll reference. That is, one must relate the face and quality to those of a known doll maker and make price judgments from that point.

QUALITY

The mark does not tell all about a doll. Two examples from the same mold could look entirely different and carry vastly different prices because of the quality of the work done on the doll, which can vary from head to head, even with dolls made from the same mold by one firm. To command top price, a bisque doll should have lovely bisque, decoration, eyes and hair. Before purchasing a doll, the collector should determine whether the example is the best available of that type. Even the molding of one head can be much sharper with more delineation of details such as dimples or locks of hair. The molding detail is especially important to notice when purchasing dolls with character faces or molded hair.

The quality of the bisque should be smooth and silky; dolls with bisque which is rough, pimply or peppered with tiny black specks would be second choices at a lower price. However, collectors must keep in mind that many heads were put out from the factories with small manufacturing defects as companies were in business for profit and were producing expendable play items, not works of art.

Since doll heads are hand-painted, the artistry of the decoration should be examined. The tinting of the complexion should be subdued and even, not harsh and splotchy. Artistic skill should be evident in the portrayal of the expression on the face and in details, such as the lips, eyebrows and eyelashes and particularly the eyes which should show highlights and shading when they are painted. On a doll with molded hair, individual brush marks to give the hair a more realistic look would be a desirable detail.

If a doll has a wig, the hair should be appropriate if not old. Dynel or

17in (43cm) J.D.K. baby with molded cap. Very rare. *Christie's, South Kensington.* (For more information see page 263.)

15in (38cm) J.D.K. 226 character baby. *Private Collection.* (For more information see page 263.)

synthetic wigs are not appropriate for antique dolls; a human hair or good quality mohair wig should be used. If a doll has glass eyes, they should have natural color and threading in the irises to give a lifelong appearance.

If a doll does not meet all of these standards, it should be priced lower than one that does. Furthermore, an especially fine example will bring a premium over an ordinary but nice model.

CONDITION

Another factor which is important when pricing a doll is the condition. A bisque doll with a crack on the face or extensive professional repair would sell for considerably less than a doll with only normal wear; a hairline or a small professional repair in an inconspicuous place would decrease the value somewhat, but not nearly so much. Sometimes a head will have a factory flaw which occurred in the

making, such as a cooking crack, scratch, piece of kiln debris or a ridge not smoothed out. Since the factory was producing toys for a profit and not creating works of art, all heads with slight flaws were not discarded, especially if they were in an inconspicuous place or could be covered. If these factory defects are slight and not detracting, they have little or no affect on the value of the doll, and whether or not to purchase such a doll would be a matter of personal opinion.

It is to be expected that an old doll will show some wear: perhaps there is a rub on the nose or cheek, or maybe a chipped earring hole; a Schoenhut doll or a Käthe Kruse may have some scuffs; an old papier-mâché may have a few age cracks; a china head may show wear on the hair; an old composition body may have scuffed toes or missing fingers. These are to be expected and do not necessarily affect the value of the doll. However, a doll in exceptional condition will bring more than "book price."

Unless an antique doll is rare or you particularly want that specific doll, do not pay top price for a doll which needs extensive work: restringing, setting eyes, repairing fingers, replacing body parts, new wig or dressing. All of these repairs add up to a considerable sum at the doll hospital, possibly making the total cost of the doll more than it is really worth.

Composition dolls in perfect condition are becoming harder to find. As their material is so susceptible to the atmosphere, their condition can deteriorate literally overnight. Even in excellent condition, a composition doll nearly always has some fine crazing or slight fading. It is very difficult to find a composition doll in mint condition and even harder to be sure that it will stay that way. However, if a composition doll is a top price, there should be little or no crazing, excellent coloring, original uncombed hair, and original clothes in excellent condition; the doll should be unplayed with. Pay less for a doll which does not have original clothes and hair or one which may be all original but shows extensive play wear. Pay even less for one which has heavy crazing and cracking or other damages.

Hard plastic and vinyl dolls must be in mint condition if they are at top price. The hair should be perfect in the original set; clothes should be completely original, fresh and unfaded. Skin tones should be natural with good cheek color.

BODY

In order to command top price, an old doll must have the original or an appropriate old body in good

24in (61cm) American Character hard plastic and vinyl *Sweet Sue* bride, all original. *H&J Foulke, Inc.* (For more information see page 62.)

condition. If a doll does not have the correct type of body, the buyer ends up not with a complete doll, but with two parts — head and body —not worth as much as one whole doll. As dolls are becoming more difficult to find, more are turning up with "put together" bodies; therefore, all parts of the body should be checked to make sure that they are appropriate to each other. A body which has mixed parts from several makers or types of bodies is not worth as much as one which has parts original to each other.

Minor damage or repair to an old body does not affect the value of an antique doll. An original body carefully repaired, recovered or even if necessary completely repainted is preferable to a new one. An antique head on a new body would be worth only the value of its parts, whatever the price of the head and new body, not the full price of an antique doll. It is just a rule of thumb that an antique head is worth about 40-50% of the price of a complete doll. A very rare head could be worth up to 80%.

If there is a choice of body types for the same bisque head, a good quality ball-jointed composition body is more desirable than a crudely made five-piece body or a stick-type body with just pieces of turned wood for upper arms and legs. Collectors prefer jointed composition bodies over kid ones for dolly-faced dolls, and pay more for the same face on a composition body.

Occasionally, the body adds value to the doll. In the case of bisque heads, a small doll with a completely jointed body, a French fashion-type with a wood-jointed body, a *Tête Jumeau* head on an adult body or a character baby head on a jointed toddler-type body would all be higher in price because of their special bodies.

As for the later modern dolls, a composition doll on the wrong body or a body in poor condition which is cracked and peeling would have a greatly reduced value. The same is true of a vinyl doll with replaced parts, body stains or chewed-off fingers.

CLOTHING

It is becoming increasingly difficult to find dolls in old clothing because as the years go by, fabrics continue to deteriorate. Consequently, collectors are paying more than "book price" for an antique doll if it has old clothes, shoes and hair. Even faded, somewhat worn, or carefully mended original or contemporary clothes are preferable to new ones. As collectors become more sophisticated and selective, they realize the value of old doll clothing and accessories. Some dealers are not specializing in these areas. Good old leather doll shoes will bring over $74 per pair; a lovely Victorian white-work doll dress can easily cost $75; an old dress for a French fashion lady $300. Good old doll wigs can bring from $25 to $250.

However, when the clothing must be replaced on an antique doll and old clothing cannot be obtained, the new clothes should be appropriately styled for the age of the doll and constructed in fabrics which would have been available when the doll was produced. There are many reference books and catalog reprints which show dolls in original clothing, and authentic patterns can be purchased.

To bring top price, a modern doll must have original clothes. It is usually fairly simple to determine whether or not the clothing is original and factory made. Some makers even placed tags in the doll's clothing. Replaced clothing greatly reduces the price of modern dolls. Without the original clothing, it is often impossible to identify a modern doll as so many were made using the same face mold.

TOTAL ORIGINALITY

Totally original dolls nowadays are becoming rare. It is often difficult to determine whether the head and body and all other parts of the doll, including wig, eyes and clothes, have always been together. Many parts of a doll could be changed and clothing and accessories could be added over the years. Many dolls labeled "all original" are simply wearing contemporary clothing and wigs. Some collectors and dealers are "embellishing" the most expensive dolls by taking original clothing and wigs from cheaper dolls to further enhance the value of the more costly ones. Dolls with trunks of clothing and in boxed sets are particularly vulnerable to this type of raiding. Collectors should examine such items carefully before they pay ultra high prices for such ensembles. Of course, when these ensembles are genuine, they are the ultimate in doll collecting.

AGE

The oldest dolls do not necessarily command the highest prices, although currently a ca. 1690 *William & Mary* wooden doll holds the world's record at $107,900. A lovely old china head with exquisite decoration and very unusual hairdo would bring a price of several thousand dollars, but not as much as a 20th century S.F.B.J. 252 pouty. Many desirable composition dolls of the 1930s and fairly recent but discontinued Alexander plastic dolls are selling at prices higher than older bisque dolls of 1890 to 1920. So in determining price, the age of the doll may or may not be significant.

SIZE

The size of a doll is usually taken into account when determining a price. Generally, the size and price for a certain doll are related: a smaller size is lower, a larger size is higher. However, there are a few exceptions on the small size. The 10in (25cm) #1 Jumeau, the 11in (28cm) *Shirley Temple*, the tiny German dolly-faced dolls on fully-jointed bodies and the 6in (9cm) *Wee Patsy* are examples of small dolls which bring higher prices than dolls in their series which may be larger.

AVAILABILITY

The price of a doll is directly related to its availability in most cases. The harder a doll is to find, the higher will be its price. Each year brings more new doll collectors than it brings newly discovered desirable old dolls; hence, the supply of old dolls is diminished. As long as the demand for certain antique and collectible dolls is greater than the supply, prices will rise. This explains the great increase in prices of less common dolls, such as the K & R and other German character children, early French dolls, early china heads and papier-mâchés, composition personality dolls, Sasha dolls, and some Alexander dolls which were made for only a limited period of time. Dolls which are fairly common, primarily the German dolly-faces and the later china head dolls which covered a long period of production, show a more gentle increase in price.

POPULARITY

There are fads in dolls just like in clothes, food and other aspects of life. Dolls which have recently risen in price because of their popularity are the Brus and the lady French fashion dolls, as well as American cloth dolls and the 8in (20cm) Alexander *Wendy* series dolls. Some dolls are popular enough to tempt collectors to pay prices higher than the availability factor warrants. Although *Shirley Temples*, Jumeaus, *Bye-Los*, K & R 101 and 114, and some plastic Alexander dolls are not rare, the high prices they bring are due to their popularity.

DESIRABILITY

Some dolls may be very rare, but they do not bring a high price because

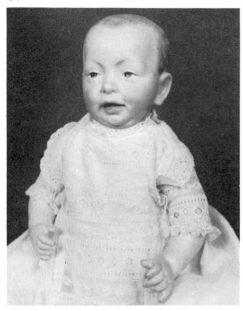

16in (41cm) K & R 100 baby. *Private Collection.* (For more information see page 251.)

they are not particularly desirable. There are not many collectors looking for them. Falling into this category are the dolls with shoulder heads made of rubber or rawhide. While an especially outstanding example will bring a high price, most examples bring very low prices in relationship to their rarity.

UNIQUENESS

Sometimes the uniqueness of a doll makes price determination very difficult. If a collector has never seen a doll exactly like it before, and it is not given in a price guide or even shown in any books, deciding what to pay can be a problem. In this case, the buyer has to use all of his available knowledge as a frame of reference in which to place the unknown doll. Perhaps a doll marked "A.M. 2000" or "S & H 1289" has been found, but is not listed in the price guide and no other examples can be found. The price is 25% higher than for the more commonly found numbers by that maker. Or perhaps a black *Kamkins* is offered for twice the price of a white one. In cases such as these, a collector must use his own judgment to determine what the doll is worth to him.

RETAIL PRICE

How does a dealer decide what price to ask for a doll? Of course, the most important factor is the price that the dealer himself had to pay for it. When buying a doll for resale, a dealer has to consider all aspects of the doll discussed in this chapter as well as whether or not there is a possibility of making a reasonable profit on the doll. A dealer, when purchasing for resale, cannot pay the amount in the price guide; he must buy somewhat lower if he expects to make a profit.

There is a great deal of competition for available old dolls. A dealer looks to estate sales, auctions, collectors and other dealers as possible doll sources, all of which are also available to collectors who can purchase from these sources at the same prices that dealers can. Contrary to what many collectors believe, dealers in antique dolls do not make enormous profits. Their margin of profit is not nearly so large as that of the proprietor of a shop which sells new items. This is primarily due to the availability factor as old dolls cannot be ordered from a wholesale catalog. Most are coming from estates or collections whose owners want to get as much as they can for their dolls.

Expenses involved in exhibiting at shows include booth rent and travel costs which are quite high. Dealers who sell by mail have high costs for advertising and having lists printed. To the price which he must pay for a doll, a dealer must figure in his costs and percentage of profit to come up with a dollar amount for the price tag. And, of course, the final price must be within an acceptable price range to a potential buyer or the dealer will not be able to sell the doll at all.

The price for a doll which is listed in the price guide is the retail value of a doll fulfilling all of the criteria discussed if it is purchased from a dealer. Collectors, however, sometimes have other sources of dolls from which the price could be somewhat lower. Sometimes collectors will sell to each other at less than "book price." Sometimes a dealer will undersell a doll if he wants to turn stock fast or if he obtains a type of doll which he does not usually carry. Then, too, collectors just might get a lucky price at an antique shop, garage sale, flea market, doll show or just about anywhere that there might be an old doll for sale.

16in (41cm) French fashion lady by Gaultier, all original. *Betty Harms Collection.* (For more information see page 175.)

20in (51cm) molded hair papier-mâché lady with side curls and coiled back braid, all original. *Pearl D. Morley Collection.* (For more information see page 325.)

Selling A Doll

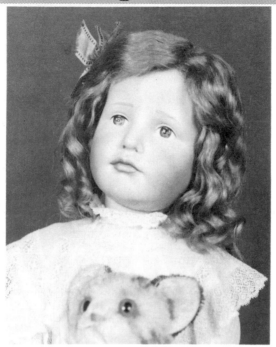

22in (56cm) K & R 114 character girl. *Private Collection.* (For more information see page 255.)

So many times we are asked by people "How do I go about selling a doll?" that it seems a few paragraphs on the topic would be in order. The first logical step would be to look through the *BLUE BOOK* to identify the doll that you have and to ascertain a retail price. Work from there to decide what you might ask for your doll. It is very difficult for a private person to get a retail price for a doll.

Be realistic about the condition. If you have a marked 18in (46cm) *Shirley Temple* doll with combed hair, no clothing, faded face with crazing and a piece off of her nose, do not expect to get book price of $600 for her because

that price would be a retail price for an excellent doll, all original, in pristine unplayed with condition if purchased from a dealer. Your very used doll is probably worth only $50 to $75 as it will have to be purchased by someone who would want to restore it.

If you have an antique doll with a perfect bisque head, but no wig, no clothes and unstrung but having all of its body parts, you can probably expect to get about half its retail value depending upon how desirable that particular doll is. If your doll has perfect bisque head with original wig, clothing, and shoes, you can probably get up to 75% of its retail value.

13in (33cm) F & B *Candy Kid*, all original. *H&J Foulke, Inc.* (For more information see page 167.)

As to actually selling the doll, there are several possibilities. Possibly the easiest is to advertise in your local paper. You may not think there are any doll collectors in your area, but there probably are. You might also check your local paper to see if anyone is advertising to purchase dolls; many dealers and collectors do so. Check the paper to find out about antique shows in your area. If anyone has dolls, ask if they would be interested in buying your doll.

You could consign your doll to an auction. If it is a common doll, it will probably do quite well at a local sale. If it is a more rare doll, consider sending it to one of the auction houses which specialize in selling dolls; most of them will accept one doll if it is a good one and they will probably get the best price for you. It would probably be worth your while to purchase a doll magazine (*Doll Reader*®, 900 Frederick St., Cumberland, MD 21502) in which you will find ads from auction houses, doll shows and leading dealers. You could advertise in doll magazines, but you might have to ship the doll and guarantee return privileges if the buyer does not like it.

If you cannot find your doll in the *BLUE BOOK*, it might be a good idea to have it professionally appraised. This will involve your paying a fee to have the doll evaluated. We provide this service and can be contacted through *Doll Reader* for which we write a regular column. Many museums and auction houses also appraise dolls.

A.T.

Maker: Possibly by A. Thuillier, Paris, France. Some heads by F. Gaultier.
Date: 1875—1893
Material: Bisque socket head on wooden, kid or composition body
Size: Size 1 is usually 9in (23cm); size 14 is 29in (74cm)
Mark:

—————— AT·N° 8 ——— A. 8 .T ——————

Marked A. T. Child: Perfect bisque head, cork pate, good wig, paperweight
eyes, pierced ears, closed mouth; body of wood, kid or composition in good
condition; appropriate clothes.

Composition body, 16—17in (41—43cm)	**$25,000****
Kid body, 26in (66cm)	**26,000****
Open mouth, 2 rows teeth, 16in (41cm)	**9,000—10,000****

**Not enough price samples to compute a reliable range.

16¼in (41cm) A. 8 T. *Courtesy of Richard W. Withington, Inc.*

Acme Toy Co.

Maker: Acme Toy Manufacturing Co., New York, N.Y., U.S.A.
Date: 1908—on
Material: Composition and cloth
Mark: ACME TOY CO.

Acme Character Baby: Ca. 1920s. Composition head, molded hair, smiling face, dimples, sleep eyes, open mouth with teeth; cloth torso, composition, bent arms and legs; original or appropriate clothes.
23—25in (59—64cm) **$250—300**

25in (64cm) Acme Toy Co. character baby, all original. Possibly *Honey* from 1929. *Leone McMullen Collection.*

Alabama Indestructible Doll

Maker: Ella Smith Doll Co., Roanoke, AL., U.S.A.
Date: 1900—1925
Material: All-cloth
Size: 11½—27in (29—69cm); 38in (96cm) black one known
Mark: On torso or leg, sometimes both:

PAT. NOV. 9, 1912.

NO. 2

ELLA SMITH DOLL CO.

or

"MRS. S. S. SMITH
Manufacturer and Dealer to
The Alabama Indestructible Doll
Roanoke, Ala.
PATENTED Sept. 26, 1905"

(also 1907 on some)

Alabama Baby: All-cloth painted with oils, tab-jointed shoulders and hips, flat derriere for sitting; painted hair (or rarely a wig), molded face with painted facial features, applied ears, (a few with molded ears); painted stockings and shoes (a few with bare feet); appropriate clothes; all in good condition, some wear acceptable.

13—14in (33—36cm)	$1400—1500
17in (43cm)	1800
22—23in (56—58cm)	2100—2300
Black,	
23in (58cm)	2500—2800**
38in (96cm)	4000—4500**

**Not enough price samples to compute a reliable average.

22in (56cm) *Alabama Baby* No. 3, Patented Sept. 26, 1905. *Betty Harms Collection.*

Madame Alexander

Maker: Alexander Doll Co., New York, N.Y., U.S.A.

Date: 1923—on, but as early as 1912 the Alexander sisters were designing doll clothes and dressing dolls commercially.

Mark: Dolls themselves marked in various ways, usually "ALEXANDER". Clothing has a white cloth label with blue lettering sewn into a seam which says "MADAME ALEXANDER" and usually the name of the specific doll. Cloth and other early dolls are unmarked and identifiable only by the clothing label.

CLOTH

Alice in Wonderland: Ca. 1930. All-cloth with one-piece arms and legs sewn on; yellow yarn hair; flat face with hand-painted features, large round eyes, O-shaped mouth; or molded mask face with large blue eyes; original dress with apron.

20in (51cm)

Fair	**$325—375**
Mint	**550—600**

Cloth Character Dolls: Ca. 1933 through the 1930s. All-cloth with one-piece arms and legs sewn on; mohair wig, molded mask face of felt or flocked fabric, painted eyes to the side, original clothes tagged with name of particular doll. Produced characters from *Little Women*, Charles Dickens, Longfellow and other literary works as well as storybook characters.

16in (41cm)

Fair	**$325—375**
Mint	**550—600**

16in (41cm) cloth character *Meg*, all original. *Vivian C. Flagg Collection.*

Cloth Baby: Ca. 1936. All-cloth with molded felt or flocked mask face, soft-stuffed stockinette body with flexible arms and legs; yarn or hair wig, painted eyes with long upper and lower eyelashes; original tagged clothes; all in good condition.

17in (43cm)   **$350—400**

Dionne Quintuplet: Brown hair and eyes, gold-colored name pin or necklace.

17in (43cm)   **$650—750**

Susie Q. & Bobby Q.: Ca. 1938. All-cloth with turning head, yellow or red yarn braids, mask face, large side-painted googly eyes, button nose, tiny closed mouth; striped stocking legs, white felt spats; original tagged clothes including hat, coat and cardboard suitcase; all in good condition. Came in sizes 12—13in (31—33cm) and 15—16in (38—41cm).

All Sizes **$550—650**

COMPOSITION

Dionne Quintuplets: 1935. All-composition with swivel head, jointed hips and shoulders, toddler or bent-limb legs; wigs or molded hair, sleep or painted eyes; original clothing, all in excellent condition.

MARK: "ALEXANDER" sometimes "DIONNE"
Clothing label:
"GENUINE
DIONNE QUINTUPLET DOLLS
ALL RIGHTS RESERVED
MADAME ALEXANDER, N.Y."
or
"DIONNE QUINTUPLET
(her name)
EXCLUSIVE LICENSEE
MADAM [sic] ALEXANDER
DOLL CO."

7—8in (18—20cm)	$ 200—225
matched set	**1250**
10in (25cm) baby	**300—350**
11—12in (28—31cm) toddler	**350—400**
14in (36cm) toddler	**450—500**
16in (41cm) toddler	**550—600**

Little Shaver: 1942. Stuffed pink stocking body, curved arms, tiny waist; floss wig glued on; mask face with large painted eyes to the side, tiny mouth; original clothes; all in excellent condition.

MARK: Cloth dress tag:
"Little Shaver
Madame Alexander
New York
All Rights Reserved."

7in (18cm)	**$225—275**
10—12in (25—31cm)	**225—275**
16in (41cm)	**350—400**
16in (41cm) baby with cloth body	**400—450**
Pins, each	**75—85**

Each Quint has her own color for clothing:
Yvonne — pink
Annette — yellow
Cecile — green
Emelie — lavender
Marie — blue

11in (28cm) Dionne Quintuplet ***Yvonne*** toddler, all original (in box). *H&J Foulke, Inc.*

Madame Alexander continued

Little Colonel: 1935. All-composition with swivel head, jointed hips and shoulders; mohair wig, sleep eyes, closed mouth, dimples; original clothes; all in excellent condition. *Betty* face.
MARK: On head: "ALEXANDER" or none
On dress tag: "Madame Alexander"
13—14in (33—36cm) **$500—550**

Foreign and Storyland: Ca. 1935 to mid 1940s. All-composition with one-piece head and body on smaller ones and separate head on larger ones, jointed shoulders and hips; mohair wig, painted eyes; original tagged clothes; all in excellent condition. Made children to represent foreign lands as well as storybook characters.
MARK: On back: "Mme. Alexander"
7—9in (18—23cm)
Foreign Countries $175—225
Storybook Characters 225—275
Birthday Dolls and other special outfits **250 up**

7in (18cm) *Jo* from "Little Women," all original in flowered box with gold label. *H&J Foulke, Inc.*

Madame Alexander continued

Dr. Dafoe: 1936. All-composition with swivel head, jointed hips and shoulders; gray wig, painted eyes, smiling face; original tagged doctor's outfit; all in excellent condition; doll unmarked.
14in (36cm) **$700—750**

14in (36cm) ***Dr. Dafoe***, all original. *Private Collection.*

Babies: 1936—on. Composition head, hands and legs, cloth bodies; molded hair or wigged, sleep eyes, open or closed mouth; original clothes; all in excellent condition.
MARK: On dolls:
    "ALEXANDER"
On clothing: "Little Genius", "Baby McGuffey", "Pinky", "Precious", "Butch", "Bitsey".
11—12in (28—31cm) **$165—185**
16—18in (41—46cm)   **225—275**
24in (61cm)   **300—350**

18in (46cm) ***Little Genius***, all original. *H&J Foulke, Inc.*

Madame Alexander continued

Jane Withers: 1937. All-composition with swivel head, jointed shoulders and hips; dark mohair wig, sleep eyes, open smiling mouth; original clothes; all in excellent condition.

MARK: On dress:

> "Jane Withers
> All Rights Reserved
> Madame Alexander, N.Y."

12-13in (31—33cm) closed mouth	**$650—750**
15—16in (38—41cm)	**750—850**
21in (53cm)	**900—1100**

Princess Elizabeth Face: All-composition, jointed at neck, shoulders and hips; mohair or human hair wig, sleeping eyes, open mouth; original clothes; all in excellent condition.

MARK: On head:

> "PRINCESS ELIZABETH
> ALEXANDER DOLL CO."

Clothing tagged with individual name of doll

Princess Elizabeth, 1937:

13in (33cm)		
Betty face	**$275**	
14—16in (36—41cm)	**325—375**	
20—22in (51—56cm)	**425—450**	
24in (61cm)	**500—525**	
27in (69cm)	**600—650**	

15in (38cm) ***Princess Elizabeth***, all original. *H&J Foulke, Inc.*

13in (33cm) unidentified Alexander girl, possibly ***Princess Elizabeth*** or ***Little Colonel*** with ***Betty*** face, all original. *H&J Foulke, Inc.*

Madame Alexander continued

McGuffey Ana, 1937 (braids):

9in (23cm) painted eyes, "Wendy" face	**250—275**
11in (28cm) closed mouth	**300—325**
13—15in (33—38cm)	**350—400**
18—20in (46—51cm)	**450—500**
24in (61cm)	**600—625**

Snow White, 1937 (closed mouth, black hair):

13in (33cm)	**300—350**
16—18in (41—46cm)	**375—450**

Flora McFlimsey, 1938 (red hair, freckles):

15in (38cm)	**550—650**

Kate Greenaway, 1938:

16—18in (41—46cm)	**475—550**

See color photograph on page 67.

9in (23cm) *McGuffey Ana* with "Wendy" face. All original with box. *H&J Foulke, Inc.*

11in (28cm) *Scarlett O'Hara*, all original. *H&J Foulke, Inc.*

Wendy Ann Face: All-composition, jointed at neck, shoulders, and hips; human hair or mohair wig, sleeping eyes, closed mouth; original clothes tagged with name of individual doll; all in excellent condition.

MARK:

"WENDY-ANN
MME ALEXANDER"

or

ALEXANDER

Wendy-Ann, 1936:

9in (23cm) painted eyes	**$250—275**
14in (36cm) swivel waist	**350—375**
21in (53cm)	**500—550**

Scarlet O'Hara, 1937 (black hair, blue or green eyes):

11in (28cm)	**350—400**
14in (36cm)	**450—475**
18in (46cm)	**550**
21in (53cm)	**600—650**

Note: Sometimes the name is spelled "Scarlet;" other times "Scarlett."

Madame Alexander continued

Bride & Bridesmaids, 1940:
14in (36cm)	**250—275**
18in (46cm)	**325—375**
21in (53cm)	**400—450**

Madelaine, 1940:
14in (36cm)	**350—400**
18in (46cm)	**450—500**

Carmen (Miranda), 1942
(black hair):
9in (23cm)	
painted eyes	**225—250**
14—15in (36—38cm)	**325—375**

Fairy Princess, 1942:
14in (36cm)	**275—325**

Fairy Queen, 1942:
18in (46cm)	**450**

Armed Forces Dolls, 1942:
WAAC, WAVE,
WAAF,and Soldier
14in (36cm)	**375—425**

14in (36cm) *Fairy Princess*, all original.
H&J Foulke, Inc.

Sonja Henie: 1939. All-composition, jointed at neck, shoulders and hips, human hair or mohair wig, sleep eyes, smiling open mouth with teeth; original clothes; all in excellent condition. 14in (35.6cm) can be found on the WENDY-ANN body with swivel waist.

MARK: On back of neck:
"MADAME ALEXANDER-
SONJA HENIE"
On dress: "Sonja Henie"
14in (36cm)	**$350—375**
18in (46cm)	**475—525**
21in (53cm)	**550—600**

14in (36cm) *Sonja Henie*, all original.
H&J Foulke, Inc.

Madame Alexander continued

Jeannie Walker: 1941. Composition, jointed at neck, shoulders and hips, with walking mechanism; human hair or mohair wig, sleep eyes, closed mouth; original clothes; all in excellent condition.

MARK: On body:

"ALEXANDER/PAT. NO.
2171281"

On dress:

"Jeannie Walker —
Madame Alexander — N.Y.,
U.S.A.
All rights reserved"

13—14in (33—36cm) **$400—425**
18in (46cm) **575**

Margaret Face: All-composition, jointed at neck, shoulders and hips; human hair, mohair, or floss wig, sleeping eyes, closed mouth; original clothes tagged with name of individual doll; all in excellent condition.

MARK: "ALEXANDER"

Margaret O'Brien, 1946
(dark braided wig):
14in (36cm) **$475—525**
18in (46cm) **650—700**
21in (53cm) **800**
Karen Ballerina, 1946
(blonde wig in coiled braids):
18in (46cm) **500—550**
Alice-in-Wonderland, 1947:
14in (36cm) **300—350**
18in (46cm) **400—450**

See color photograph on page 67.

18in (46cm) ***Karen Ballerina***, all original.
H&J Foulke, Inc.

Madame Alexander continued

HARD PLASTIC

Margaret Face: 1948—on. All-hard plastic, jointed at neck, shoulders and hips; lovely wig, sleep eyes, closed mouth; original clothes tagged with name of doll; all in excellent condition.

MARK: "ALEXANDER"

Nina Ballerina, 1949—1951
14in (36cm) **$300—325**
18in (46cm) **375—400**

Fairy Queen, 1947—1948
14in (36cm) **275—300**

Babs, 1948—1949
14in (36cm) **325—350**

Margaret Rose, 1948—1953?
14in (36cm) **275—300**

Margaret O'Brien, 1948
14in (36cm) **500—600**

Wendy-Ann, 1947—1948
18in (46cm) **350—375**

Wendy Bride, 1950
14in (36cm) **275—300**

Cinderella, 1950
14in (36cm) **550—600**

Prince Charming, 1950
14in (36cm) **600**

Cynthia (black), 1952—1953
14in (36cm) **550**

Story Princess, 1954—1956
14in (36cm) **350—375**

Wendy (from Peter Pan set), 1953
14in (36cm) **450**

Prince Philip, Ca. 1950
18in (46cm) **500—600**

Snow White, 1952
14in (36cm) **500**

Bride, 1952
18in (46cm) **350—375**

Margot Ballerina, 1953
18in (46cm) **375—400**

Glamour Girls, 1953
18in (46cm) **$650—700**

Queen Elizabeth, 1953
18in (46cm) **650—700**

Godey Ladies, 1950
14in (36cm) **700—750**

Me and My Shadow, 1954
18in (46cm) **550—600**

18in (46cm) *Nina Ballerina*, all original. *Private Collection.*

Maggie Face: 1948—1956. All-hard plastic, jointed at neck, shoulders and hips; good quality wig, sleep eyes, closed mouth; original clothes tagged with the name of the doll; all in excellent condition.

MARK: "ALEXANDER"

Maggie, 1948—1953
14in (36cm) **$250—300**
17in (43cm) **325—350**

Madame Alexander continued

Polly Pigtails, 1949
  14in (36cm)   **325—350**
Kathy, 1951
  14in (36cm)   **350—375**
Alice in Wonderland, 1950—1951
  14in (36cm)   **300—325**
  17in (43cm)   **375—400**
Annabelle, 1952
  17in (43cm)   **375—425**
Peter Pan, 1953   **450—475**
Rosamund Bridesmaid, 1953
  15in (38cm)   **300—325**
Glamour Girls, 1953
  18in (46cm)   **650—700**
Me and My Shadow, 1954
  18in (46cm)   **550—600**
Godey Man, 1950
  14in (36cm)   **700—750**

18in (46cm) **Victoria** from "Me & My Shadow" series, all original. *H&J Foulke, Inc.*

Little Women: 1948—1956. All-hard plastic, jointed at neck, shoulders and hips; synthetic wig, sleep eyes, closed mouth; original clothes; all in excellent condition. Some models have jointed knees. "Maggie" and "Margaret" faces.
MARK: On head:
  "ALEXANDER."
On clothes tag:
  "Meg", "Jo", "Beth",
  "Amy", and "Marme"
14—15in (36—38cm)
  Floss hair,
    1948—1950   **$ 300—350**
    matching set of 5 dolls **1600**
  Amy loop curls   **375—400**
    Dynel wig   **250—275**
Little Men: Tommy, Nat
  and **Stuffy**, 1952   **750 up each**

14in (36cm) **Amy**, all original with floss hair and loop curls. *H&J Foulke, Inc.*

Madame Alexander continued

Little Genius: Ca. 1950. Hard plastic head, sleeping eyes, mohair wig; cloth body with hard plastic hands and legs; original tagged clothes; all in excellent condition.

12in (28cm)	**$165—185**
16—18in (41—46cm)	**225—275**
24in (61cm)	**300—350**

24in (61cm) ***Little Genius***, all original. *H&J Foulke, Inc.*

Winnie and Binnie: 1953—1955. All-hard plastic, walking body, later with jointed knees and vinyl arms; lovely wig, sleep eyes, closed mouth; original clothes; all in excellent condition.

15in (38cm)	**$250—275**
18in (46cm)	**275—300**
24in (61cm)	**350—400**

Cissy: 1955—1959. Head, torso and jointed legs of hard plastic, jointed vinyl arms; synthetic wig, sleep eyes, closed mouth, pierced ears; original clothes; all in excellent condition.

MARK: On head: "ALEXANDER"
On dress tag: "Cissy"

21in (53cm)

Street clothes	**$300—350**
Gowns	**400 up***
Elaborate fashion gowns	**600 up***

*Depending upon costume.

Madame Alexander continued

Little Genius: 1956—1962. Hard plastic head with short curly wig, sleep eyes, drinks and wets; vinyl torso, arms and legs; original clothes; all in excellent condition.
8in (20cm) **$185**

Elise: 1957—1964. All-hard plastic with vinyl arms, completely jointed; synthetic wig, sleep eyes, closed mouth; original clothes; all in excellent condition.
16½—17in (42—43cm)

Street clothes	**$250—300**
Bride, Ballerina	**300—350**
Gowns	**325 up***

*Depending upon costume.

16½in (42cm) *Elise*, all original. *Private Collection.*

Lissy: 1956—1958. All-hard plastic, jointed at neck, shoulders, hips, elbows and knees; synthetic wig, sleep eyes, closed mouth; original clothes; all in excellent condition.
MARK: None on doll
On dress tag:
"Lissy" or name of character

12in (31cm)	**$ 350—375**
Kelly, 1959	**375—425**
Little Women, 1957—1967	**250—300**
Katie and Tommy, 1962	**1000—1200**
McGuffey Ana, 1963	**1000—1200**
Laurie, 1967	**500**

12in (31cm) basic *Lissy*, all original. *H&J Foulke, Inc.*

Madame Alexander continued

Cissette: 1957—1963. All-hard plastic, jointed at neck, shoulders, hips and knees; synthetic wig, sleep eyes, closed mouth, pierced ears; original clothes; all in excellent condition.

MARK: None on doll
On dress tag: "Cissette"

10in (25cm)	$ 200 up*
Margot, 1961	375—425
Sleeping Beauty, 1960s	375—425
Jacqueline, 1962	550—600
Gibson Girl, 1963	1000—1200
Gold Rush, 1963	1250—1400
Pamela with wigs & trousseau gift set	525
Portrettes, 1968—1973	450—550
Jenny Lind, 1969—1970	600

*Depending upon costume.

10in (25cm) Cissette *Melanie* Portrette, all original. *Virginia Ann Heyerdahl Collection.*

Madame Alexander continued

Alexander-Kins: All-hard plastic, jointed at neck, shoulders and hips; synthetic wig, sleep eyes, closed mouth; original clothes; all in excellent condition.
7½—8in (19—20cm)
1953, straight leg non-walker
1954—1955, straight leg walker
1956—1964, bent-knee walker
1965—1972, bent knee
1973—current, straight leg
1978, face change
1981, white face
MARK: On back of torso: "ALEX"
After 1978: "MADAME ALEXANDER"
On dress tag:
"Madame Alexander"
"Alexander-Kins" or specific name of doll
Wendy, in dresses
1953—1972 $ 300 up
Wendy Ballerina,
1956—1973   250 up
Quizkin,
1953   400
Little Lady   400—450

Special Outfits:
Scarlett O'Hara,
1965—1972
print dress   **400—500**
Enchanted Doll,
1980—1981   **375—400**
Korea, Africa, Hawaii,
Vietnam, Spanish Boy,
Greek Boy, Morocco,
Equador, Bolivia   **400**
Amish Boy and Girl,
Cowboy, Cowgirl, English
Guard, Pocahontas, Hiawatha,
Colonial   **500**
Bent-knee
Internationals   **95—110**
Storybooks   **110—125**
Little Women   **125—135**
Maggie Mixup   **450**
Nurse   **550 up**
Prince Charles   **500 up**
Romeo   **900**
Aunt Pittypat   **1500**
Cousin Grace   **1200**
Guardian Angel   **850**

8in (20cm) **Beth**, 1955 bent-knee walker, all original. *H&J Foulke, Inc.*

8in (20cm) **Nurse**, all original. *Private Collection.*

Madame Alexander continued

Kelly Face: 1958—on. Vinyl character face with rooted hair, vinyl arms, hard plastic torso and legs, jointed waist; original clothes; all in excellent condition.

MARK: On head:

Kelly, 1958—1959 15in (38cm)	**$250**
Pollyana, 1960—1961 15in (38cm)	250
Marybel, 1959—1965 15in (38cm), in case	275
Edith, 1958—1959 15in (38cm)	250

15in (38cm) **Marybel**, all original. *H&J Foulke, Inc.*

Shari Lewis: 1959. All-hard plastic with slim fashion body; auburn hair, brown eyes, closed mouth; original clothes; all in excellent condition.
14in (36cm) **$350**
21in (53cm)   450—475

Maggie Mixup: 1960—1961. All-hard plastic, fully-jointed; red straight hair, green eyes, closed mouth, freckles; original clothes; all in excellent condition.
8in (20cm)   **$450**
16½—17in (42—43cm) 325—375

See color photograph on page 65.

Betty: 1960. Vinyl and hard plastic with rooted hair, smiling face; walking body; original tagged clothes; all in good condition.
30in (76cm) **$350—400**

30in (76cm) **Betty**, with original wrist tag. *H&J Foulke, Inc.*

Jacqueline: 1961—1962. Vinyl and hard plastic; rooted dark hair, sleep eyes, closed mouth; original clothes; all in excellent condition.

21in (53cm)	**$700—750**

Portrait Dolls,
1965 to present, 21in (53cm)

Scarlett, green velvet or taffeta 1975—1982	**325**
Melanie, 1967—1974	**500**
Renoir, 1965—1973	**600**
Bride, 1969	**600**
Mimi, 1971	**550**
Gainsborough, 1972	**550**
Gainsborough, 1978	**450**
Agatha, 1974—1981	**350—400**
Scarlett, red velvet, 1965	**900**

See color photograph on page 65.

21in (53cm) *Gainsborough,* 1972 Portrait, all original. *Private Collection.*

Caroline: 1961—1962. Hard plastic and vinyl; rooted blonde hair, smiling character face; original clothes; in excellent condition.

15in (38cm)   **$325—350**

Janie: 1964—1966. Vinyl and hard plastic with rooted hair, impish face, pigeon-toed and knock-kneed; original tagged clothes; all in excellent condition.

12in (31cm)	**$275**
Lucinda, 1969—1970	**350**
Rozy, 1969	**400**
Suzy, 1970	**400**

Smarty: 1962—1963. Hard plastic and vinyl, smiling character face with rooted hair, knock-kneed and pigeon-toed; original clothes; in excellent condition.

12in (31cm)	**$250—275**
Katie (black), 1965	**400—450**

12in (31cm) *Smarty,* all original. *H&J Foulke, Inc.*

Madame Alexander continued

Polly Face: All-vinyl with rooted hair, jointed at neck, shoulders and hips; original tagged clothes; all in excellent condition.

17in (43cm):

Polly, 1965	**$250—275***
Leslie (black), 1965—1971	**300—350***

*Allow extra for ballgowns.

See color photograph on page 66.

Sound of Music: Large set 1965-1970; small set 1971—1973. All dolls of hard plastic and vinyl with appropriate synthetic wigs and sleep eyes; original clothes; all in excellent condition.

MARK: Each doll tagged as to character.

Small set

8in	(20cm)	*Friedrich*	$225
8in	(20cm)	*Gretl*	200
8in	(20cm)	*Marta*	200
10in	(25cm)	*Brigitta*	225
12in	(31cm)	*Maria*	300
10in	(25cm)	*Louisa*	375
10in	(25cm)	*Liesl*	300

Large set*

11in	(28cm)	*Friedrich*	275
11in	(28cm)	*Gretl*	225
11in	(28cm)	*Marta*	225
14in	(36cm)	*Brigitta*	225
17in	(43cm)	*Maria*	350
14in	(36cm)	*Louisa*	300
14in	(36cm)	*Liesl*	250

*Allow considerably more for sailor outfits.

11in (28cm) *Friedrich* with "Janie" face, all original. *Private Collection.*

Madame Alexander continued

Mary Ann Face: Introduced in 1965 and used widely to present a variety of dolls. Only discontinued dolls are listed here. Vinyl head and arms, hard plastic torso and legs; appropriate synthetic wig, sleep eyes; original clothes; all in excellent condition.

MARK: On head:

"ALEXANDER
19©65"

14in (35cm) only:

Madame,	
1967—1975	$ 300
Mary Ann, 1965	250
Orphant Annie,	
1965—1966	300
Gidget, 1966	250
Little Granny, 1966	200
Riley's Little Annie,	
1967	300

Renoir Girl,	
1967—1971	250
Easter Girl, 1968	1200
Scarlett #1495,	
1968	500
Jenny Lind & Cat,	
1969—1971	350
Jenny Lind, 1970	450
Grandma Jane,	
1970—1972	225
Disney Snow White,	
to 1977	500
Goldilocks,	
1978—1982	100

Coco: 1966. Vinyl and hard plastic, rooted blonde hair, jointed waist, right leg bent slightly at knee; original clothes; all in excellent condition. This face was also used for the 1966 portrait dolls.
21in (53cm) **$1800 up**

Elise: 1966 to present. Vinyl face, rooted hair; original tagged clothes; all in excellent condition.

17in (43cm)	$150*
Portrait Elise, 1973	300
Marlo, 1967	500
Maggie, 1972—1973	300

*Discontinued styles only.

14in (35cm) *Grandma Jane*, all original. *Private Collection.*

21in (53cm) *Coco*, 1966 Portrait, all original. *Private Collection.*

Madame Alexander continued

Nancy Drew Face: Introduced in 1967 and used widely to present a variety of dolls. Only discontinued dolls are listed here. Vinyl head and arms, hard plastic torso and legs; appropriate synthetic wig, sleep eyes; original clothes; all in excellent condition.

12in (31cm) only:

Nancy Drew, 1967	**$225**
Renoir Child, 1967	**250**
Blue Boy, 1972—1983	**110**
Lord Fauntleroy, 1981—1983	**125**

Peter Pan Set: 1969. Vinyl and hard plastic with appropriate wigs and sleep eyes; original clothes; all in excellent condition.

14in (36cm) *Peter Pan* ("Mary Ann" face)	**$250—275**
14in (36cm) *Wendy* ("Mary Ann" face)	**250—275**
12in (31cm) *Michael* ("Jamie" face)	**350**
11in (28cm) *Tinker Bell* ("Cissette")	**350**

First Ladies: Hard plastic and vinyl with rooted synthetic hair individually styled and sleep eyes; original tagged clothes; in mint condition. "Martha" and "Mary Ann" faces.

14in (36cm)

Series I: 1976—1978
Martha Washington, Abigail Adams, Martha Randolph, Dolley Madison, Elizabeth Monroe and *Louisa Adams.*

Set:	**$950**
Individual:	**150**
Martha Washington	**250**

Series II: 1979—1981
Sarah Jackson, Angelica Van Buren, Jane Findlay, Julia Tyler, Sarah Polk and *Betty Taylor Bliss.*

Set:	**$650**
Individual:	**110**

Series III: 1982—1984
Jane Pierce, Abigail Fillmore, Mary Todd Lincoln, Martha Johnson Patterson, Harriet Lane and **Julia Grant.**

Set:	**$550**
Individual:	**90**
Mary Todd Lincoln:	**125**

14in (36cm) *Sarah Jackson*, First Ladies Series II with "Martha" face. *H&J Foulke, Inc.*

All-Bisque Dolls
(So-Called French)

Maker: Various French and/or German firms
Date: Ca. 1880—on.
Material: All-bisque
Size: Various small sizes, under 12in (31cm)
Mark: None, sometimes numbers

All-Bisque French Doll: Jointed at shoulders and hips, swivel neck, slender arms and legs; good wig, glass eyes, closed mouth; molded shoes or boots and stockings; appropriately dressed; all in good condition, with proper parts.

4½—5in (12—13cm)	**$ 600—650***
5½—6in (14—15cm)	**650—700***
With bare feet,	
5—6in (13—15cm)	**700—800***
With jointed elbows and knees,	
5—6in (13—15cm)	**2200****
With jointed elbows,	
5—6in (13—15cm)	**1600****
Oriental,	
5in (13cm)	**900****
Pierced-in ears,	
6in (15cm)	**1000***

*Allow extra for original clothes.
**Not enough price samples to compute a reliable range.

5in (13cm) French-type all-bisque with bare feet. *H&J Foulke, Inc.*

All-Bisque Dolls
(German)

Maker: Various German firms
Date: Ca. 1880—on
Material: Bisque
Size: Various small sizes, most under 12in (31cm)
Mark: Some with "Germany" and/or numbers; some with paper labels on stomachs

---

All-Bisque French-type: Ca. 1880—on. Jointed usually by wire or pegging at shoulders and hips, stationary neck, slender arms and legs; good wig, glass eyes, closed mouth; molded shoes or boots and stockings; dressed or undressed; all in good condition, with proper parts.

3in (8cm)	**$185**
3½-4in (9—10cm)	**160—200**
5in (13cm)	**250**
6in (15cm)	**300**
7in (18cm)	**350—375**

Swivel neck:

3½—4in (9—10cm)	**275—325**
6—6½in (15—17cm)	**400—450**

Black or Mulatto:

4—4½in (10—12cm)	**250—275**

4¼in (11cm) French-type all-bisque with swivel neck. *H&J Foulke, Inc.*

All-Bisque with painted eyes: Ca. 1880—on. Jointed at shoulders and hips, stationary neck; molded and painted hair or mohair wig, painted eyes, closed mouth; molded and painted shoes and stockings; fine quality work; dressed or undressed; all in good condition, with proper parts.

1¼in (3cm)	**$ 65—75**
1½—2in (4—5cm)	**75—85**
4—5in (10—13cm)	**130—165**
6—7in (15—18cm)	**185—210**

Swivel neck:

2½in (9cm)	**125—150**
4—5in (10—13cm)	**175—225**

Early round face, bootines:

6—7in (15—18cm)	**325—350**
8½in (22cm)	**450—475**

8½in (22cm) fine early all-bisque with round face, painted eyes, pegged arms and stiff hips. *Joanna Ott Collection.*

All-Bisque Dolls (German) continued

All-Bisque with molded clothes:
Ca. 1890—on. Many by Hertwig
& Co. Jointed only at shoulders,
molded and painted clothes or
underwear; molded and painted
hair, sometimes with molded hat,
painted eyes, closed mouth;
molded shoes and socks (if in
underwear often barefoot); good
quality work; all in good condition, with proper parts.

Children:

4—5in (10—13cm)	**$125—150**
6—7in (15—18cm)	**200—225**

Early-style characters,
jester and clown,

4—5in (10—13cm)	275—325

Punch, Judy and
other white bisque
characters,

3—4in (8—10cm)	**95—110**

6½in (17cm) all-bisque boy by Hertwig &
Co. *H&J Foulke, Inc.*

Hatted dolls, see page 178.

All-Bisque with glass eyes: Ca.
1890—on. Very good quality
bisque, jointed at shoulders,
stiff or jointed hips; good wig,
glass eyes, closed mouth (sometimes open); molded and painted
shoes and stockings; dressed or
undressed; all in good condition,
with proper parts.

3in (8cm)	**$185**
4—5in (10—13cm)	**185—225**
7in (18cm)	**300—350**
8in (20cm)	**425—450**
9in (23cm)	**575—625**
11in (28cm)	**800—850**
12in (31cm)	**900—950**

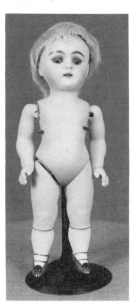

8¼in (21cm) all-bisque 184/11 with glass
eyes. *H&J Foulke, Inc.*

All-Bisque Dolls (German) continued

All-Bisque with swivel neck and glass eyes: Ca. 1880—on. Swivel neck, pegged shoulders and hips; good wig, glass eyes, closed mouth; molded and painted shoes or boots and stockings; dressed or undressed; all in good condition, with proper parts.

4in (10cm)	$ 260—295
5—6in (13—15cm)	325—375
7in (18cm)	425—475
8in (20cm)	575—625
10in (25cm)	900—950
Early Kestner or S&H type:	
6—7in (15—18cm)	800—850*
9—10in (23—25cm)	1250—1500*
With jointed knee:	
10in (25cm)	2500**
So-called "Wrestler" (#102):	
8½in (22cm)	1100*

*Allow extra for original clothes.
**Not enough price samples to compute a reliable range.

See color photograph on page 68.

8½in (22cm) all-bisque so-called "Wrestler," swivel neck, molded black boots. *Betty Harms Collection.*

8in (20cm) all-bisque 190 with swivel neck and glass eyes. *H&J Foulke, Inc.*

7½in (19cm) early Kestner-type all-bisque with blue molded boots. *Yvonne Baird Collection.*

All-Bisque Dolls (German) continued

All-Bisque with long black or blue stockings: Ca. 1890—on. Jointed at neck, shoulders and hips; good wig, glass sleep eyes, open mouth with teeth; molded brown shoes and molded long black or blue stockings; dressed or undressed; all in good condition, with proper parts. Sometimes marked "S & H 886" or "890."

4½in (12cm), closed mouth	**$450***
5½—6in (14—15cm)	**525—575**
7—7½in (18—19cm)	**650—700**

*Allow extra for original clothes.

All-Bisque Baby: 1900—on. Jointed at shoulders and hips with curved arms and legs; molded and painted hair, painted eyes; not dressed; all in good condition, with proper parts.

2½—3½in (6—9cm)	**$ 60—75**	
4—5in (10—13cm)	**110—135**	

Fine early quality, blonde molded hair:

4½in (12cm)	**125—150**
6—7in (15—18cm)	**175—225**
13in (33cm)	**750**
10½in (27cm) glass eyes, swivel neck	**1500****

**Not enough price samples to compute a reliable range.

6¼in (16cm) all-bisque with long black stockings, remains of original clothes. *H&J Foulke, Inc.*

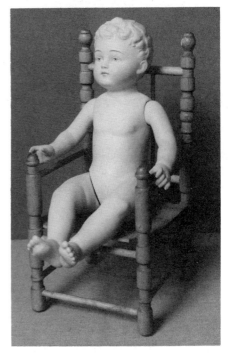

13in (33cm) all-bisque baby, fine early quality. *Joanna Ott Collection.*

All-Bisque Dolls (German) continued

All-Bisque Character Baby: Ca. 1910. Jointed at shoulders and hips, curved arms and legs; molded hair, painted eyes, character face; undressed; all in good condition, with proper parts.

4in (10cm)	**$125—150**
6in (15cm)	**185—225**
8in (20cm)	**375—425**
With glass eyes, 4—5in (10—13cm)	**250—285**
Swivel neck, glass eyes:	
6in (15cm)	**375—425**
10in (25cm)	**650—750**
11½in (29cm)	**850—950**
Toddler, swivel neck, glass eyes, 7½in (19cm)	**600**

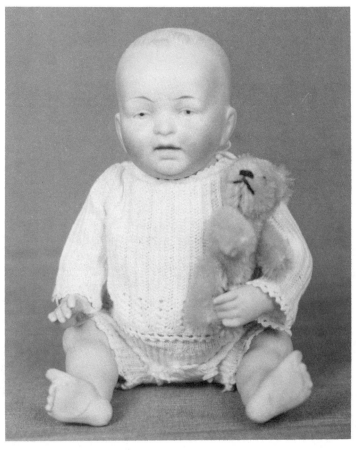

8in (20cm) all-bisque character baby with painted eyes. *Private Collection.*

All-Bisque Dolls (German) continued

All-Bisque Character Dolls: 1913—on. Character faces with well-painted features and molded hair; usually jointed only at arms. Also see individual listings.

Chin Chin (Heubach), 4in (10cm)	$ 225—250
Small pink bisque characters (many by Hertwig & Co.),	
up to 3in (8cm)	40
3in (8cm) glass eyes	75
6in (13cm)	60
Orsini, MiMi or DiDi, 5in (13cm)	1000—1100
ViVi, 5in (13cm)	1200
HEbee SHEbee, 4½in (12cm)	300
Happifats boy or girl, 4½in (12cm)	225
Our Fairy, wig and glass eyes, 9in (23cm)	1500—1600
Teenie Weenie, 4in (10cm)	125**
Little Annie Roonie, 4in (10cm)	225
Scootles, 6in (13cm)	450
Girl, side-glancing eyes, molded braids, 5in (13cm)	250—275

**Not enough price samples to compute a reliable average.

See color photographs on pages 68 and 69. .

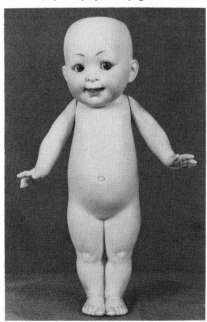

12in (31cm) *Our Fairy. Richard Wright Antiques.*

4in (10cm) *Teenie Weenie* stamped in black on foot "W. Donahey © 1922," orange or blue suit and shoes. *H&J Foulke, Inc.*

All-Bisque Dolls (German) continued

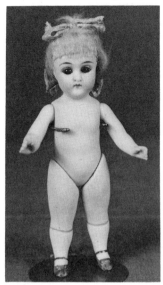

7in (18cm) all-bisque with glass eyes, 1915-type. *H&J Foulke, Inc.*

Later All-Bisque with glass eyes:
Ca. 1915. Jointed at shoulders and hips; good wig, glass eyes, closed or open mouth; molded and painted black one-strap shoes and stockings; undressed or dressed; all in good condition, with proper parts.

4—5in (10—31cm)	**$125—150**
7in (18cm)	**225—250**
8in (20cm)	**275—300**

All-Bisque with character face:
Ca. 1915. Jointed at shoulders and hips; smiling character face, closed or open mouth; molded and painted black one-strap shoes and stockings; dressed or undressed; all in good condition, with proper parts.

Painted eyes, molded hair, 5in (13cm)	**$150—175**
#150 open/closed mouth with two painted teeth, 4½in (12cm)	**185—200**
6in (15cm) glass eyes	**250—285**
9in (23cm) glass eyes	**750**
5—5½in (13—14cm) painted eyes	**160—185**
Kestner type, swivel neck, glass eyes, 4½—5½in (12—14cm)	**400—500**
#155, smiling face, 5½in (14cm)	**350—375**

See color photograph on page 68.

5½in (14cm) all-bisque 155 character with smiling face. *H&J Foulke, Inc.*

All-Bisque Dolls (German) continued

Later All-Bisque with painted eyes: Ca. 1920. Jointed at shoulders and hips, stationary neck; mohair wig or molded hair, painted eyes, closed mouth; molded and painted one-strap shoes and white stockings; dressed or undressed; all in good condition, with proper parts.

3in (8cm) $ 50—60
4½—5in (12—13cm) 80—90
6—7in (15—18cm) 125—160

All-Bisque "Flapper" (tinted bisque): Ca. 1920. Jointed at shoulders and hips; molded bobbed hair with loop for bow, painted features; long yellow stockings, one-strap shoes with heels; undressed or dressed; all in good condition, with proper parts, very good quality.

4—5in (10—13cm) $225—275
6—7in (15—18cm) 300—375
Standard quality, 5in (13cm) 135—165

3in (8cm) all-bisque with painted eyes. *H&J Foulke, Inc.*

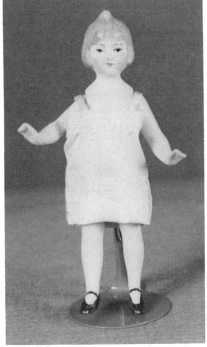

5in (13cm) 127 flapper with tinted bisque and long yellow stockings. *H&J Foulke, Inc.*

All-Bisque Dolls (German) continued

2¾in (7cm) pink bisque *Candy* baby, all original. *H&J Foulke, Inc.*

All-Bisque Baby: Ca. 1920. Pink bisque, jointed at shoulders and hips, curved arms and legs; painted hair, painted eyes; original factory clothes; all in good condition, with proper parts.

2½—3in (6—8cm)   **$ 60—65**
8in (20cm)   **125**

All-Bisque "Flapper:" Ca. 1920. Pink bisque with wire joints at shoulders and hips; molded bobbed hair and painted features; painted shoes and socks; original factory clothes; all in good condition, with proper parts.

3in (8cm)   **$ 40—45**
Molded hats   **135—165**

3in (8cm) flapper doll with molded hat bunny ears, all original. *H&J Foulke, Inc.*

All-Bisque Dolls (German) continued

All-Bisque Nodder Characters:
Ca. 1920. Many made by Hertwig
& Co. Nodding heads, elastic
strung, molded clothes; all in
good condition. Decoration is
usually not fired so it wears and
washes off very easily. Marked
Germany.
3—4in (8—10cm) $ 45
German Comic Characters,
    3—4in (8—10cm) **75 up**

3½in (9cm) all-bisque nodders. *H&J Foulke, Inc.*

All-Bisque Immobiles: Ca. 1920. All-bisque figures with molded clothes,
molded hair and painted features. Decoration is not fired, so it wears and
washes off very easily. Marked Germany.
Tinies: adults and children, 1½—2¼in (4—6cm) **$25—30**
Children, 3¼in (8cm)   **30—35**
Bride & Groom, 4—5in (10—13cm)   **55—65**
Santa, 3in (8cm)   **85—95**

All-bisque tiny immobile family. *H&J Foulke, Inc.*

All-Bisque Dolls
(Made in Japan)

Maker: Various Japanese firms
Date: Ca. 1915—on
Material: Bisque
Size: Various small sizes
Mark: "Made in Japan" or "NIPPON"

6in (15cm) girl with molded bobbed hair.
H&J Foulke, Inc.

Baby Doll with bent limbs: Jointed shoulders and sometimes hips; molded and painted hair and eyes; not dressed; all in good condition.

White, 4in (10cm) **$ 25**
Black,
4—5in (10—13cm) **35—45**
Betty Boop-type,
4—5in (10—13cm) **15—20**
6—7in (15—18cm) **25—30**
Child,
4—5in (10—13cm) **20—25**
6—7in (15—18cm) **30—35**
Comic Characters,
3—4in (8—10cm) **25 up***
Stiff Characters,
3—4in (8—10cm) **5—8**
6—7in (15—18cm) **20—25**
Cho-Cho San,
4½in (12cm) **65—75**
Nodders,
4in (10cm) **25—30**
Orientals,
3—4in (8—10cm) **20—25**
Queue San,
4in (10cm) **65—75**
Marked "Nippon" Characters,
4—5in (10—13cm) **35—45**
Three Bears boxed set **110—135**

*Depending upon rarity.

4in (10cm) nodder children. *Dolly Valk Collection.*

Alma

Maker: Unknown manufacturer, Turin, Italy
Date: 1929—on
Material: All-felt
Mark: Cloth label, cardboard tag; sometimes stamp on foot

Alma Doll: All-felt with swivel head, jointed shoulders and hips; painted features, eyes usually side-glancing, mohair sewn on head, distinctive curled felt ear; original intricate clothing; in excellent condition.
16—19in (41—48cm) **$600—700**

19in (48cm) Alma doll, all original and boxed. *Esther Schwartz Collection.*

Alt, Beck & Gottschalck

Maker: Alt, Beck & Gottschalck, porcelain factory, Nauendorf near Ohrdruf, Thüringia, Germany. Made heads for many producers including Wagner & Zetzsche.

Date: 1854—on

Material: China and bisque heads for use on composition, kid or cloth bodies; all-bisque or all-china dolls.

18in (46cm) china shoulder head 784. *H&J Foulke, Inc.*

China Shoulder Head: Ca. 1880. Black or blonde-haired china head; old cloth body with china limbs or kid body; dressed; all in good condition. Mold numbers, such as *784, 1000, 1008, 1028, 1046, 1142, 1210,* etc.

MARK: *1 0 0 8 ✕ 9*

Also ✕ or ✕₀ in place of ✕

10in (25cm)	**$175—200**
15—18in (38—46cm)	**275—300**
20—22in (51—56cm)	**350—400**
25in (64cm)	**450**

16½in (42cm) bisque shoulder head 1288 with glass eyes. *H&J Foulke, Inc.*

Bisque Shoulder Head: Ca. 1880. Molded hair, painted or glass eyes, closed mouth; cloth body with bisque lower limbs; dressed; all in good condition. Mold numbers, such as *890, 1000, 1008, 1028, 1064, 1142, 1254, 1288.*

MARK: See above

Painted eyes,

12—13in (31—33cm)	**$210—235***
15—18in (38—46cm)	**275—350***
20—23in (51—58cm)	**400—450***

Glass eyes,

18—20in (46—51cm)	**550—650***

*Allow extra for unusual or elaborate hairdo or molded hat.

Alt, Beck & Gottschalck continued

All-Bisque Girl: 1911. Chubby body, loop strung shoulders and hips, inset glass eyes, open/closed mouth, painted eyelashes, full mohair or silky wig; molded white stockings, blue garters, black Mary Janes.

MARK:

8 3
---
2 2 5
2-4

Also *#100, 125* or *150* in place of *225*.
Bottom number is centimeter size.

5in (13cm)	$165—175
7in (18cm)	235—265
8in (20cm)	300—325
10in (25cm)	550

Character: 1910—on. Perfect bisque head, good wig, sleep eyes, open mouth; some with open nostrils; composition body; all in good condition; suitable clothes.

MARK: See below (child doll)
#1322, 1352, 1361
(For photograph, see
5th Blue Book, page 2.)

10—12in (25—31cm)	$325—375*
15—18in (38—46cm)	475—550*
23—24in (58—61cm)	750—850*

#1357
(For photograph, see
7th Blue Book, page 55.)

18—20in (46—51cm) toddler	750—800**

#1358
(For photograph, see
7th Blue Book, page 180.)

18—20in (46—51cm)	2800**

*Allow $50 extra for flirty eyes or toddler body.
**Not enough price samples to compute a reliable average.

10in (25cm) 83/225/24 all-bisque girl.
H&J Foulke, Inc.

Alt, Beck & Gottschalck continued

Bisque Shoulder Head: Ca. 1885—on. Turned shoulder head, mohair or human hair wig, plaster dome or bald head, glass sleeping or set eyes, closed mouth; kid body with gusseted joints and bisque lower arms, dressed; all in good condition. Mold numbers, such as *639, 698, 1123, 1235.*

MARK: 6 3 9 ✕ 6 with DEP after 1888

15—17in (38—43cm)	**$ 550—600**
20—22in (51—56cm)	**700—800**
26in (66cm)	**1000**

With open mouth:

MARK: 6 9 8 ½ *Germany Dep Nᵒ 10*

14—16in (36—41cm)	**$400—425**
20—22in (51—56cm)	**450—475**
25in (64cm)	**550—575**

Child Doll: 1914—on. Perfect bisque head, good wig, sleep eyes, open mouth; ball-jointed body in good condition; appropriate clothes. Mold *#1362.*

MARK:

11—12in (28—31cm)	**$ 300—325**	
16—18in (41—46cm)	**375—425**	
21—24in (53—61cm)	**450—550**	
29—31in (74—79cm)	**850—950**	
36in (91cm)	**1400—1500**	
39—42in (99—107cm)	**2200—2500**	

16in (41cm) 639 bisque turned shoulder head. *Yvonne Baird Collection.*

11in (28cm) ABG 1362 child. *H&J Foulke, Inc.*

Louis Amberg & Son

Maker: Louis Amberg & Son, New York, N.Y., U.S.A.

Date: 1907—on (although Amberg had been in the doll business under other names since 1878)

Jointed Girl: 1912. Composition dolly face head, sleeping eyes, open mouth, human hair wig; jointed composition body; all in good condition with appropriate clothes. (For photograph see *7th Blue Book*, page 56.)

MARK: Body:

> "AMBERG
> VICTORY
> DOLL"

Head: "L.A. &S"

22—24in (56—61cm)   **$250—275**

New Born Babe: 1914, reissued 1924. Designed by Jeno Juszko. Bisque head of an infant with painted hair, sleep eyes, closed mouth; soft cloth body with celluloid, rubber or composition hands; appropriate clothes; all in good condition. (For photograph see *6th Blue Book*, page 55.)

MARK: "© L.A.&S. 1914, G 45520 Germany #4", also "Heads copyrighted by LOUIS AMBERG and Son", also "© L. Amberg & Son Germany 886/2"

Length:

8in (20cm)	**$325**
10—12in (25—31cm)	**400—450**
14—15in (36—41cm)	**550—650**

Charlie Chaplin: 1915. Composition portrait head with molded and painted hair, painted eyes to the side, closed full mouth, molded mustache; straw-filled cloth body with composition hands; original clothes; all in good condition with wear.

MARK: cloth label on sleeve:

> "CHARLIE CHAPLIN DOLL
> World's Greatest Comedian
> Made exclusively by Louis Amberg
> & Son, N.Y.
> by Special Arrangement with
> Essamay Film Co."

14in (36cm)   **$400—450**

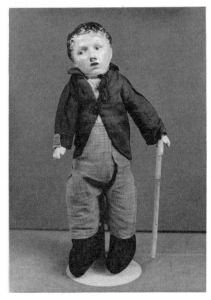

14in (36cm) *Charlie Chaplin*, all original. *Yvonne Baird Collection.*

Louis Amberg & Son continued

Composition Mibs: 1921. Composition shoulder head designed by Hazel Drucker with wistful expression, molded and painted blonde or reddish hair, blue painted eyes, closed mouth; cloth body with composition arms and legs with painted shoes and socks; appropriate old clothes; all in good condition. (For photograph see *5th Blue Book*, page 43.)

MARK: None on doll; paper label only:

"Amberg Dolls
Please Love Me
I'm Mibs"

16in (41cm) **$450—500**

All-Bisque Mibs: 1921. Molded and painted features, jointed at shoulders and sometimes hips; painted shoes and socks; undressed; all in good condition.

MARK: Sometimes on back:

"©
LA&S 1921
Germany"

or paper label on chest:

'Please
Love Me
I'm
MIBS"

3in (8cm)   **$225**
4¾in (12cm)   **300—325**

3in (8cm) all-bisque *Mibs. H&J Foulke, Inc.*

Baby Peggy: 1923. Composition head, arms and legs, cloth body; molded brown bobbed hair, painted eyes, smiling closed mouth; appropriately dressed; all in good condition.

20in (51cm) **$500—550****
**Not enough price samples to compute a reliable range.

Baby Peggy: 1924. Perfect bisque head with character face; brown bobbed mohair wig, brown sleep eyes, closed mouth; composition or kid body, fully-jointed; dressed or undressed; all in very good condition. (For photograph see *7th Blue Book*, page 58.)

MARK:

"19 © 24
LA & S NY
Germany
—50—
982/2"

also:
973 (smiling socket head)
972 (pensive socket head)
983 (smiling shoulder head)
982 (pensive shoulder head)
18—22in (46—56cm) **$2400—2750**

Louis Amberg & Son continued

All-Bisque Baby Peggy: 1924. Smiling face with painted brown bobbed hair or sometimes brown mohair wig, painted eyes, closed mouth; jointed arms and legs; brown strap shoes and socks; undressed; all in excellent condition. Unmarked, but had a paper label on stomach.

3in (8cm) **$225**
5½in (14cm) **300—325**

5½in (14cm) all-bisque *Baby Peggy*. *H&J Foulke, Inc.*

All-Bisque Character Children: 1920s. Made by a German porcelain factory. Pink pretinted bisque with molded and painted features, molded hair; jointed at shoulders and hips; molded stockings with blue garters, brown strap shoes, white stockings.

5—6in (13—15cm) **$150—175**
7½in (19cm) girl
with molded bow **250—275**

7½in (19cm) all-bisque character girl with molded hair bow. *H&J Foulke, Inc.*

6½in (17cm) all-bisque character boy. *H&J Foulke, Inc.*

Vanta Baby: 1927. A tie-in with Vanta baby garments. Composition or bisque head with molded and painted hair, sleep eyes, open mouth with two teeth (closed mouth and painted eyes in all-composition small dolls); muslin body jointed at hips and shoulders, curved composition arms and legs; suitably dressed; all in good condition.

MARK:

"VANTA BABY -- AMBERG"

20in (51cm):
Composition head **$200—225**
Bisque head **650—700**

Louis Amberg & Son continued

Sue, Edwina or It: 1928. All-composition with molded and painted hair, painted eyes; jointed neck, shoulders and hips, a large round ball joint at waist; dressed; all in very good condition.
MARK:
"AMBERG
PAT. PEND.
L.A. & S. © 1928"
14in (36cm)   **$350—400**

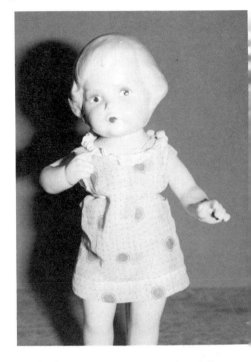

14in (36cm) *It, Sue* or *Edwina*, repainted features. *Doodlebug Doll & Toy Shop.*

Tiny Tots Body Twists: 1928. All-composition with jointed shoulders and a large round ball joint at the waist; molded and painted hair in both boy and girl styles, painted eyes; painted shoes and socks; dressed; all in good condition.
MARK: tag on clothes:
"An Amberg Doll with
BODY TWIST
all its own
PAT. PEND. SER. NO.
32018"
8in (20cm)   **$165—175**

8in (20cm) *Body Twist. Kay & Wayne Jensen Collection.*

American Character

Maker: American Character Doll Co., New York, N.Y., U.S.A.
Date: 1919—on
Trademark: Petite

Sally: 1930. All-composition jointed at neck, shoulders and hips; molded and painted hair, painted side-glancing eyes, closed mouth; original or appropriate clothes; all in good condition.
MARK:

               "PETITE
               SALLY"

12in (31cm)	**$150—175**
16in (41cm) sleeping eyes	**200—225**

12in (31cm) pair of *Sally* twins, all original. *H&J Foulke, Inc.*

American Character continued

Marked Petite Mama Dolls: 1923—on. Composition head, arms and legs, cloth torso; mohair or human hair wig, sleep eyes, closed mouth; original clothes; all in good condition. (For photograph see *7th Blue Book*, page 61.)

16—18in (41—46cm) **$165—185**
24in (61cm) **225—250**

Marked Petite Girl Dolls: 1930s. All-composition jointed at neck, shoulders and hips; human hair or mohair wig, lashed sleeping eyes, open mouth with teeth; original or appropriate old clothes; all in good condition.

16—18in (41—46cm) **$175—200**
24in (61cm) **250**

18in (46cm) all-composition *Petite Girl,* all original. *H&J Foulke, Inc.*

Puggy: 1928. All-composition chubby body jointed at neck, shoulders and hips; molded and painted hair, painted eyes to the side, closed mouth, pug nose, frowning face; original clothes; all in good condition. (For photograph see *7th Blue Book*, page 61.)
MARK: "A PETITE DOLL"
12in (31cm) **$425—475**

Sweet Sue: 1953. All-hard plastic or hard plastic and vinyl, some with walking mechanism, some fully-jointed including elbows, knees and ankles; original clothes; all in excellent condition.
MARKS: Various, including: "A.C.", "Amer. Char. Doll", "American Character" in a circle.

14in (36cm) **$110—135**
18—20in (46—51cm) **160—175**
24in (61cm) **200—225**

20in (51cm) *Sweet Sue,* all original. *Miriam Blankman Collection.*

American Character continued

Eloise: Ca. 1955. All-cloth with molded face, painted side-glancing eyes, smiling mouth, yellow yarn hair; flexible arms and legs; original clothing; in excellent condition. Designed by Bette Gould from the fictional little girl "Eloise" who lived at the Plaza Hotel in New York City.
MARK: Cardboard tag
21in (53cm)   **$225**

21in (53cm) *Eloise* in two original dresses; the left one is a Christmas dress with tree design on the front. *Esther Schwartz Collection.*

Betsy McCall: 1957. All-hard plastic with legs jointed at knees; rooted saran hair on a wig cap, round face with sleep eyes, plastic eyelashes; original clothes; all in excellent condition.
MARK:
8in (20cm)   **$95—110**

8in (20cm) *Betsy McCall*, all-hard plastic. *Private Collection.*

Betsy McCall: 1960. All-vinyl with rooted hair, lashed sleep eyes, round face, turned-up mouth; slender arms and legs; original clothes; all in excellent condition. (For photograph see *7th Blue Book*, page 62.)

14in (36cm)	**$135**
20in (51cm)	**160—175**
30—36in (76—91cm)	**225—275**

Max Oscar Arnold

Maker: Max Oscar Arnold (doll and porcelain factory), Neustadt, Thuringia, Germany.

Date: 1877—on for dolls; 1919—1931 for porcelain heads (Some made for Welsch & Co., Sonneberg.)

Mark:

⟨MOA⟩

——————————— Made in Germany ———————————

Marked M.O.A. Child Doll: Perfect bisque socket head, original or appropriate wig, set or sleep eyes, open mouth; ball-jointed composition body; dressed; entire doll in good condition. Mold *150* or *200*.

16—18in (41—46cm) **$325—375***

25—26in (64—66cm) **500—525***

*Do not pay as much for a doll with poor bisque.

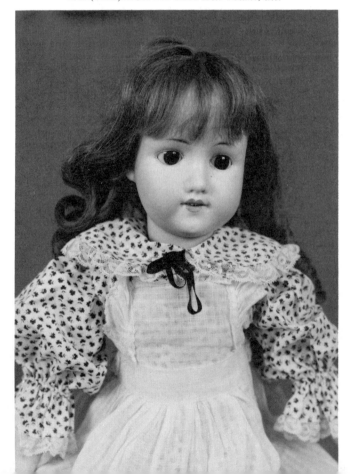

25in (64cm) *MOA* 200 child. *H&J Foulke, Inc.*

8in (20cm) Alexander hard plastic **Maggie Mixup** with her dog "Danger," all original. For further information see page 36. *Private Collection.*

21in (53cm) Alexander 1970 **Melanie**, all original. For further information see page 37. *Virginia Heyerdahl Collection.*

17in (46cm) Alexander *Leslie*, all original. For further information see page 38. *H&J Foulke, Inc.*

ABOVE: 17in (46cm) Alexander *Margaret O'Brien*, all original. For further information see page 29. *Rosemary Dent Collection.*

RIGHT: 16in (41cm) Alexander *McGuffey Ana*, all original. For further information see page 26. *Beth Foulke Collection. .*

LEFT: 8½in (22cm) unmarked all-bisque with swivel neck and glass eyes, unusual stockings with blue stripe, fine early quality. For further information see page 44. *Roberts Collection.*

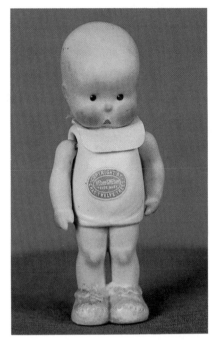

ABOVE: 4¼in (11cm) all-bisque *HE-bee SHE-bee.* For further information see page 47. *H&J Foulke, Inc.*

LEFT: 5¾in (15cm) all-bisque Kestner character child. For further information see page 48. *H&J Foulke, Inc.*

4in (10cm) all-bisque **Little Annie Rooney**. For further information see page 47. *H&J Foulke, Inc.*

12in (31cm) Babyland Rag **Topsy-Turvy**, all original. For further information see page 88. *H&J Foulke, Inc.*

ABOVE: 28in (71cm) R.D. For further information see page 339. *Betty Harms Collection.*

RIGHT: 21in (53cm) early Bru child with incised circle dot mark. For further information see page 103. *Private Collection.*

ABOVE: 18in (46cm) all-cloth Chad Valley *Princess*, all original. For further information see page 125. *Esther Schwartz Collection.*

LEFT: 14in (36cm) Bru fashion lady incised "D," all original. For further information see page 102. *Yvonne Baird Collection.*

19in (48cm) pink tinted china head with brown eyes, all original. For further information see page 128. *Yvonne Baird Collection.*

RIGHT: 27in (69cm) Art Fabric Mills print cloth girl. For further information see page 134. *Private Collection.*

ABOVE: 12in (31cm) printed cloth girl. For further information see page 134. *Private Collection.*

RIGHT: 16in (41cm) cloth Grace Drayton ***Dolly Dingle***. For further information see page 150. *H&J Foulke, Inc.*

20in (51cm) B.F. child by Danel. For further information see page 144. *Joanna Ott Collection.*

24in (61cm) DEP child with open mouth. For further information see page 146. *Joanna Ott Collection.*

LEFT: 21in (53cm) Effanbee Original Historical Doll *1760 Pre-Revolutionary*, all original. For further information see page 164. *Rosemary Dent Collection.*

BELOW: 16in (41cm) E.D. child. For further information see page 154. *Private Collection.*

LEFT: 14in (36cm) Effanbee Historical Doll Replica *1840 Covered Wagon Days*, all original. For further information see page 164.

ABOVE: 14in (36cm) Effanbee *Skippy.* For further information see page 161. *Yvonne Baird Collection.*

LEFT: 21in (53cm) French fashion lady with kid body, all original. For further information see page 171. *Yvonne Baird Collection.*

RIGHT: 15½in (39cm) unmarked French fashion lady, all original. For further information see page 171. *Private Collection.*

BELOW: 25in (64cm) F. Gaultier fashion lady. For further information see page 175. *Yvonne Baird Collection.*

LEFT: 21in (53cm) F. Gaultier child incised "F.G." in block letters. For further information see page 176. *Yvonne Baird Collection.*

BELOW: 24in (61cm) early German bisque child with open/closed mouth and molded teeth. For further information see page 258. *Private Collection.*

19in (48cm) unmarked German bisque child. For further information see page 179. *H&J Foulke, Inc.*

12in (31cm) Heinrich Handwerck
79 child, all original. For further
information see page 212. *Private
Collection.*

21in (53cm) 136 child, probably by Hertel,
Schwab & Co. For further information see
page 179. *H&J Foulke, Inc.*

30in (76cm) Heinrich Handwerck brown
child. For further information see page 95.
India Stoessel Collection.

13in (33cm) Gebrüder Heubach 5636 character child. For further information see page 222. *Private Collection.*

Arranbee

Maker: Arranbee Doll Co., New York, N.Y., U.S.A.
Date: 1922—1960
Mark: "ARRANBEE" or "R & B"

Baby: 1924. Perfect solid dome bisque head with molded and painted hair, sleep eyes, open mouth with teeth, dimples; cloth body with celluloid or composition hands, may have a molded celluloid bottle in hand, "Nursing Bottle Baby;" dressed; all in good condition.
Head circumference: 12—13in (31—33cm) **$375—425**

My Dream Baby: 1924. Perfect bisque head with solid dome and painted hair, sleep eyes, closed or open mouth; all-composition or cloth body with composition hands; dressed; all in good condition. Some heads incised *"A.M.," "341"* or *"351"*; some incised "ARRANBEE."
Head circumference:

10in (25cm)	**$275**
12—13in (31—33cm)	**350—425**
15in (38cm)	**600—650**

13in (33cm) open-mouth baby with bisque head incised "ARRANBEE." *Joanna Ott Collection.*

Storybook Dolls: 1930s. All-composition with swivel neck, jointed arms and legs; molded and painted hair, painted eyes; all original storybook costumes; all in good condition.
10in (25cm) **$150**

Nancy: 1930. All-composition, jointed at neck, shoulders and hips, molded hair, painted eyes and closed mouth; original or appropriate clothes; all in good condition.
MARK: "ARRANBEE" or "NANCY"

12in (31cm)	**$150—175**
16in (41cm) sleep eyes	**200—225**

Nancy with original trunk and wardrobe. *H&J Foulke, Inc.*

Arranbee continued

Debu'Teen: 1938—on. All-composition or composition swivel shoulder head and limbs on cloth torso; mohair or human hair wig, sleep eyes, closed mouth, original clothes; all in good condition.

MARK: "R & B"

14in (36cm)	**$150—165**
18in (46cm)	**185—200**
21in (53cm)	**225—250**
Skating doll, 14in (36cm)	**165—185**

Nancy Lee: 1940s. All-composition with jointed neck, shoulders and hips; mohair or human hair wig, sleep eyes, closed mouth; original clothes; all in good condition. This face mold was also used for dolls which were given other names.

MARK: "R & B"

14in (36cm)	**$150—165**
21in (53cm)	**225—250**

21in (53cm) **Nancy Lee**, all original. *Private Collection.*

Nanette: 1950s. All-hard plastic, jointed at neck, shoulders and hips; synthetic wig, sleep eyes, closed mouth; original clothes; all in excellent condition. This face mold was also used for dolls which were given other names.

MARK: "R & B"

14in (36cm)	**$135—150**
18in (46cm)	**175—200**

14in (36cm) **Nanette**, all original. *H&J Foulke, Inc.*

Georgene Averill
(Madame Hendren)

Maker: Averill Mfg. Co. and Georgene Novelties, Inc., New York, N.Y., U.S.A.

Date: 1915—on

Designer: Georgene Averill (See also Maud Tousey Fangel and Grace Drayton)

Trademarks: Madame Hendren

Tagged Mme. Hendren Character: Ca. 1915—on. Composition character face, usually with painted features, molded hair or wig (sometimes yarn); hard-stuffed cloth body with composition hands; original clothes often of felt, included Dutch children, Indians, sailors, cowboys, blacks; all in good condition.

10—14in (25—36cm) **$110—135**

Mama & Baby Dolls: Ca. 1918—on. Composition shoulder head, lower arms and legs, cloth torso with cry box; mohair wig or molded hair, sleep eyes, open mouth with teeth or closed mouth; appropriately dressed; all in good condition. Names such as **Baby Hendren, Baby Georgene** and others. (For photographs see *7th Blue Book*, page 197 and *6th Blue Book*, page 176.)

15—18in (38—46cm) **$135—165**
22—24in (56—61cm) **200—250**

Dolly Reckord: 1922. Composition shoulder head, lower arms and legs, cloth torso with record player; nice human hair wig, sleep eyes, open mouth with upper teeth; appropriate clothes; all in good condition with records. (For photograph see *6th Blue Book*, page 193.)

26in (66cm) **$450—475**

Infant Baby Dolls: Ca. 1924. Composition infant head with flange neck, painted hair, sleeping eyes, closed mouth; soft cloth body with composition hands; appropriately dressed. Good condition with light crazing. Sometimes stamped on body.

MARK:
> Genuine
> Madame Hendren
> Doll
> 522
> Made in U.S.A.

16in (41cm) **$125—140**
22in (56cm) **185**

Madame Hendren infant doll with stamped body. *Hazel Scherf Collection.*

Georgene Averill (Madame Hendren) continued

Whistling Doll: 1925—1929. Composition head with molded hair, side-glancing eyes, mouth pursed to whistle through round opening; composition arms, cloth torso; legs are coiled spring bellows covered with cloth; when head is pushed down or feet are pushed up, the doll whistles. Original or appropriate clothes; all in good condition. (For additional photograph see *7th Blue Book*, page 198.)

MARK: None

Original Cardboard Tag:

"I whistle when you dance me on one foot and then the other.
Patented Feb. 2, 1926
Genuine Madame Hendren Doll."

14—15in (36—38cm)

sailor, cowboy, cop or boy

(Dan)	**$150—165**
Black *Rufus* or	
Dolly Dingle	**250—300**

Bonnie Babe: 1926. Bisque heads by Alt, Beck & Gottschalck; cloth bodies by K & K Toy Co.; distributed by George Borgfeldt, New York. Perfect bisque head with smiling face, molded hair, glass sleep eyes, open mouth with two lower teeth; cloth body with composition arms (sometimes celluloid) and legs often of poor quality; all in good condition. Mold *#1368* or *1402.*

MARK: Copr. by
Georgene Averill
Germany
1005/3652
1368

Head circumference:

9—10in (23—25cm)	**$600—650**
12—13in (31—33cm)	**750—800**
Celluloid head,	
16in (41cm) tall	**450—500**

Whistling black doll with original tag. *Courtesy of Jackie Brown.*

12in (31cm) long, 8¾in (22cm) head circumference *Bonnie Babe. Private Collection.*

All-Bisque Bonnie Babe: 1926. Jointed at neck, shoulders and hips; smiling face with glass sleeping eyes, open mouth with two lower teeth; pink or blue molded slippers. Unmarked except for round paper label on stomach.

4½in (12cm)	**$600—650**
7in (18cm)	**850—950**

Body Twists: 1927. All-composition, jointed at neck, shoulders and hips, with a large round ball joint at waist; molded and painted hair, painted eyes, closed mouth; dressed; all in good condition. Advertised as *Dimmie* and *Jimmie.* (For photographs see *5th Blue Book*, page 170 and *4th Blue Book*, page 161.)

14½in (37cm) **$300**

Georgene Averill (Madame Hendren) continued

Sunny Boy and Girl: Ca. 1927. Celluloid head with molded hair and glass eyes; stuffed body with composition arms and legs; appropriate or original clothes; all in good condition.
15in (38cm) **$250—300****

****Not enough price samples to compute a reliable range.

Snookums: 1927. Composition shoulder head, molded and painted hair with hole for one tuft of hair, painted eyes, smiling face with open/closed mouth; composition yoke and arms; cloth body and legs; dressed; all in good condition. From the comic strip "The Newlyweds" by George McManus. (For photograph see *5th Blue Book*, page 169.)
14in (36cm) **$275—325**

Patsy-Type Girl: 1928. All-composition, jointed at neck, shoulders, and hips; molded hair, sleeping eyes, tiny closed mouth; bent right arm; original or appropriate old clothing; good condition with light crazing.
MARK: A.D. Co.
14in (36cm) **$165—185**

14in (36cm) Averill girl, replaced clothing. *H&J Foulke, Inc.*

Harriet Flanders: 1937. All-composition with jointed neck, shoulders and hips; chubby toddler body; solid dome head with tufts of molded blonde hair, lashed sleeping eyes, closed mouth; original clothes. Very good condition. Designed by Harriet Flanders. (For photograph see *7th Blue Book*, page 167.)
MARK: HARRIET © FLANDERS
16in (41cm) **$250**
Painted eyes, 12in (31cm) **150**

Cloth Dolls: Ca. 1930s—on. Mask face with painted features, yarn hair, painted and/or real eyelashes; cloth body with movable arms and legs; attractive original clothes; all in excellent condition.

Children or Babies:

12in (31cm)	**$ 85—125**
24—26in (61—66cm)	**175—200**

Topsy & Eva,

10in (25cm)	**125—135**

International and Costume Dolls:

12in (31cm)	**50—60**
Mint in box with wrist tag	**70—80**

(For photograph see *7th Blue Book,* page 166.)

Characters, 14in (36cm):

Little Lulu, 1944	**300****
Nancy, 1944	**350—400****
Sluggo, 1951	**350—400****
Tubby Tom, 1951	**350—400****

**Not enough price samples to compute a reliable range.

TOP RIGHT: 40in (100cm) *Little Lulu,* all original. Very rare size. *Courtesy of Lana Norlin.*

12in (31cm) *Hansel* and *Gretel,* all original in box; lid and side also shown. *Esther Schwartz Collection.*

Baby Bo Kaye

Maker: Composition heads by Cameo Doll Co.; bisque heads made in Germany, by Alt, Beck, & Gottschalck; bodies by K & K Toy Co., New York, N.Y., U.S.A.

Date: 1925

Material: Bisque, composition or celluloid head with flange neck; composition or celluloid limbs, cloth body

Designer: J. L. Kallus

Mark:

"Copr. by
J. L. Kallus
Germany
1394/30"

Baby Bo Kaye: Perfect bisque head marked as above, molded hair, glass eyes, open mouth with two lower teeth; body as above; dressed; all in good condition. (For photograph see *7th Blue Book*, page 73.)

18—19in (46—48cm)   **$2500—2700**
Celluloid or composition: 16in (41cm)   **550—600****

**Not enough price samples to compute a reliable range

All-Bisque Baby Bo Kaye: Molded hair, glass sleep eyes, open mouth with two teeth; swivel neck, jointed shoulders and hips; molded shoes and socks; unmarked.

MARK: As shown
6in (15cm) **$1250—1500****

**Not enough price samples to compute a reliable range.

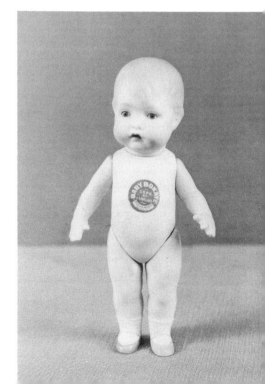

6in (15cm) all-bisque *Baby Bo Kaye.*
H&J Foulke, Inc.

Babyland Rag

Maker: E. I. Horsman, New York, N.Y., U.S.A
Date: 1904—1920
Material: All-cloth
Size: 12—30in (31—76cm)
Mark: None

Babyland Rag: Cloth face with hand-painted features, later with printed features, sometimes mohair wig; cloth body jointed at shoulders and hips; original clothes.

Early hand-painted face:
13—15in (33—38cm)
very good	**$750—850***
fair	**350—400**
22in (56cm) fair	**450**

30in (76cm)
very good	**1500—1600****

Life-like face:
13—15in (33—38cm)
very good	**550—600***

Topsy Turvy,
13—15in (33—38cm)
good	**650—750***

Black,
20in (51cm)	**900—1000***

*Allow more for mint condition doll.
**Not enough price samples to compute a reliable range.

See color photograph on page 69.

15in (38cm) Babyland Rag *Dutch Boy* and *Girl*, life-like face of 1907. *Yvonne Baird Collection.*

Bähr & Pröschild

Maker: Bähr & Pröschild, porcelain factory, Ohrdruf, Thüringia, Germany. Made heads for Bruno Schmidt, Heinrich Stier, Kley & Hahn and others.

Date: 1871—on

Material: Bisque heads for use on composition or kid bodies, all-bisque dolls

---

Marked Belton-type Child Doll: Ca. 1880. Perfect bisque head, solid dome with flat top having 2 or 3 small holes, paperweight eyes, closed mouth with pierced ears; wood and composition jointed body with straight wrists; dressed; all in good condition. Mold numbers in *200* series.

MARK: 204

13—14in (33—36cm)	**$1000—1200**
17—19in (43—48cm)	**1400—1600**
#244, Indian 13—15in (33—38cm)	**750—850**

Marked Child Doll: 1888—on. Perfect bisque shoulder or socket head, sleeping eyes, open mouth with 4 or 6 upper teeth, good human hair or mohair wig; gusseted kid or jointed composition body (many of French-type); dressed; all in good condition. Mold numbers in *200* and *300* series.

MARK: 224
      dep

#224, 239, 275, 277, 325, 379 and other socket heads:

12—14in (31—36cm)	**$550—650**
18—22in (46—56cm)	**700—750**
25in (64cm)	**850**

#246, 309 and other shoulder heads:

16—18in (41—46cm)	**375—425**
22—24in (56—61cm)	**500—575**
29in (74cm)	**850—900**

TOP RIGHT: 4in (10cm) 325 socket head with swivel neck on shoulder plate. *H&J Foulke, Inc.*

11½in (29cm) black bisque 277 dep. *Private Collection.*

Bähr & Pröschild continued

Marked B. P. Character Child:
Ca. 1910. Perfect bisque socket
head, good wig, sleep or painted
eyes, closed mouth; toddler or
jointed composition body; dressed; all in good condition. Mold
#2072, 536 and other child **500**
series. Models made for Kley &
Hahn and Bruno Schmidt.
MARK:

15—16in (36—38cm)	**$2700—2900**
19—21in (48—53cm)	**3700—4300**

15in (38cm) 546 child made for Kley &
Hahn. *Jane Alton Collection.*

Marked B. P. Character Baby: Ca. 1910—on. Perfect bisque socket head,
solid dome or good wig, sleep eyes, open mouth; composition bent-limb
baby body; dressed; all in good condition. Mold **#585, 604, 624, 678, 619,
641** and **587.**
MARK: See above

10—12in (25—31cm)	**$350—400***
16—18in (41—46cm)	**475—575***
22—24in (56—61cm)	**700—800***
26in (66cm)	**950—1000***

*Allow extra for a toddler body.

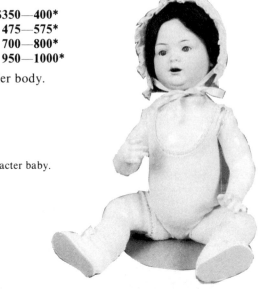

16½in (42cm) B.P. 585 character baby.
H&J Foulke, Inc.

E. Barrois

Maker: E. Barrois, doll factory, Paris, France. Heads purchased from an unidentified French or German porcelain factory.

Date: 1844—1877

Material: Bisque or china head, cloth or kid body (some with wooden arms)

Mark:

E. (DÉPOSÉ B.

E.B. Fashion Lady: Perfect bisque shoulder head (may have a swivel neck), glass eyes (may be painted with long painted eyelashes), closed mouth; appropriate wig; kid body with jointed wood arms; appropriate clothing. All in good condition.

14—15in (36—38cm) **$2300—2500**

Painted eyes, painted short black curly hair with brush marks,

20—21in (51—53cm) **2800—3000**

14in (36cm) E.B. fashion lady, kid body with wood arms. *Elizabeth McIntyre.*

Belton-type
(So-called)

Maker: Various French and German firms, such as Bähr & Pröschild
Date: 1875—on
Material: Bisque socket head, ball-jointed wood and composition body with straight wrists
Mark: None, except sometimes numbers

Belton-type Child Doll: Perfect bisque socket head, solid but flat on top with two or three small holes for stringing, paperweight eyes, closed mouth, pierced ears; wood and composition ball-jointed body with straight wrists; dressed; all in good condition.

Fine early quality
(French-type face):
    14—15in (36—38cm)**$1500—1650**
    18—20in (46—51cm) **1950—2150**
    22in (56cm)   **2400**
Tiny with five-piece body:
    8—9in (20—23cm)   **550—650**
Standard quality
(German-type face):
    10—12in (25—31cm) **850—1000**
    14—16in (36—41cm) **1200—1400**
    18—20in (46—51cm) **1550—1750**

TOP RIGHT: 8in (20cm) Belton-type child with 5-piece body. *H&J Foulke, Inc.*

13in (33cm) Belton-type child, standard quality. *H&J Foulke, Inc.*

C. M. Bergmann

Maker: C. M. Bergmann doll factory of Waltershausen, Thüringia, Germany; heads manufactured for this company by Armand Marseille, Simon & Halbig, Alt, Beck & Gottschalck and perhaps others.

Date: 1888—on

Material: Bisque head, composition ball-jointed body

Trademarks: Cinderella Baby (1897), Columbia (1904)

Mark:

C.M. BERGMANN
⁴/₀

C. M. Bergmann
Waltershausen
Germany
1916
6½ a

Bergmann Child Doll: Ca. 1889—on. Marked bisque head, composition ball-jointed body, good wig, sleep or set eyes, open mouth; dressed; all in nice condition.

18—20in (46—51cm)	$ 400—425
23—25in (58—64cm)	475—575
28—30in (71—76cm)	750—850
35in (89cm)	1150
39in (99cm)	1800

23in (58cm) C.M. Bergmann child. *H&J Foulke, Inc.*

Bergmann Character Baby: 1909—on. Marked bisque socket head, mohair wig, sleep eyes, composition bent-limb baby body; dressed; all in good condition.

12—15in (31—38cm)	$425—500**
#612 (open/closed mouth) 14—16in (36—41cm)	700—800**

**Not enough price samples to compute a reliable range.

Bing Art Dolls

Maker: Bing Werke (Bing Kunstlerpuppen) Nürnberg, Germany
Date: 1921—1932
Material: All-cloth or composition head and cloth body
Size: 6—17½in (15—45cm)
Designer: Prof. Vogt of Nürnberg & Emil Wagner of Sonneberg
Mark: "Bing" on sole of shoe or unmarked

Bing Art Doll: Cloth or composition head, molded face, handpainted
features, painted hair or wigged; cloth body with pin jointed shoulders and
hips; original clothing; very good condition.

6—7in (15—18cm) composition head	**$125—150****
10—12in (25—31cm) cloth head, painted hair	**400—500****
wigged	**300—400****

**Not enough price samples to compute a reliable range.

12in (31cm) Bing-type child marked "Made in Germany" on body. *Yvonne Baird Collection.*

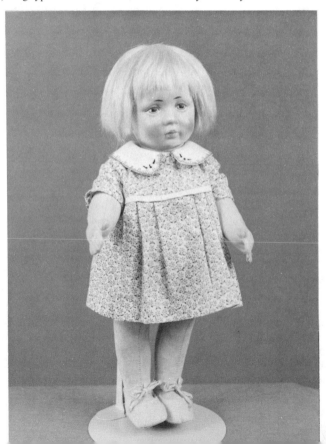

Black Dolls*

Black Bisque Doll: Ca. 1880—on. Various French and German manufacturers from their regular molds or specially designed ones with Negroid features. Perfect bisque socket head either painted dark or with dark coloring mixed in the slip, this runs from light brown to very dark; composition or sometimes kid body in a matching color, cloth bodies on some baby dolls; appropriate clothes; all in good condition.

FRENCH Makers:

Bru, Circle Dot, 16—20in (41—51cm)	**$18,000—23,000****
Jumeau, open mouth, 14—16in (36—41cm)	**1800—2000**
SFBJ/Unis 60, 12—14in (31—36cm)	**325—375**
Jules Steiner, open mouth, 14—16in (36—41cm)	**2200—2500**
Jules Steiner, closed mouth "A" series, 14in (36cm)	**4000**

GERMAN Makers (Child Dolls):

AM 390, 18in (46cm)	**450—475**
B.P. 277, 12—14in (31—36cm)	**550—650**
K★R, 13in (33cm)	**500—550**
H. Handwerck, 15—16in (38—41cm)	**650—750**
24in (61cm)	**1150**
Simon & Halbig, 20in (51cm)	**900—1000**
739, 24in (61cm)	**1300**
8in (20cm), 5-piece body	**350**
Unmarked, good quality	
10—13in (25—33cm), jointed body	**350—400**
8—9in (20—23cm), 5-piece body	**250—275**
5in (13cm), closed mouth	**225—275**
Kestner 134, 13in (33cm)	**500—550**
Kühnlenz 34, 7—8in (18—20cm), 5-piece body	**300—350**
8in (20cm), fully-jointed	**400—425**
All-bisque, glass eyes, 4in (10cm)	**250—275**
Swivel neck "61" character, 5in (13cm)	**600**

GERMAN Makers (Character Dolls):

A.M. 341 or *351,* 11in (28cm) long	**350**
14in (36cm) long	**500**
18in (46cm) long	**800**
362, 15in (38cm) baby	**575**
E. Heubach 399 or *458*, 8—9in (20—23cm)	**325—350**
418 wide grinning mouth, 10in (25cm)	**550**
463 or *444*, 14in (36cm)	**600—650**
414 toddler, 13in (33cm)	**575—600**
JDK Hilda, 12in (33cm) baby	**3000**
17in (43cm)	**4500**
K & R 101, 15—16in (38—41cm)	**3000**
K★R 100, 11in (28cm)	**650—750**
126, 10—12in (25—31cm)	**450—550**

Black Dolls continued

S PB H Hanna, 8—10in (20—25cm)	**275—325**
S&H 1358, 18in (46cm)	**4200—4600**
F.S. & Co. 1297, 10in (25cm)	**450**
R.A. 138, 15in (38cm)	**600**

**Not enough price samples to compute a reliable range.

*See also entries for specific doll makers.

See color photographs on pages 79 and 273.

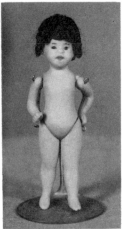

4in (10cm) brown all-bisque child with glass eyes. *H&J Foulke, Inc.*

15in (38cm) Recknagle 138 baby. *Leone McMullen Collection.*

9in (23cm) A.M. 971 toddler. *H&J Foulke, Inc.*

Black Dolls continued

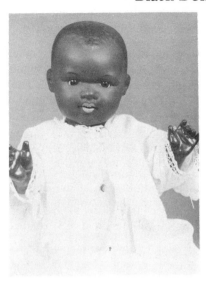

20in (51cm) A.M. 362 character baby. *Leone McMullen Collection.*

13in (33cm) Heubach Köpplesdorf 414 toddler. *H&J Foulke, Inc.*

14in (36cm) J.D.K. **Hilda**. *Leone McMullen Collection.*

21in (53cm) S & H 1079. *Gladyse Hills Hilsdorf Collection.*

Black Dolls continued

Papier-Mâché Black Doll: Ca. 1890. By various German manufacturers. Papier-mâché character face, arms and legs, cloth body; glass eyes; original or appropriate clothes; all in good condition.

10—12in (25—31cm)   **$250—300**
16—20in (41—51cm)   **500—600**
Hottentots
7½—8½in (19—24cm)   **110—140**

Tony Sarg's Mammy Doll: Composition character face with wide smiling mouth, painted features; large composition hands and molded shoes; cloth body; original clothes, carrying a white baby; all in good condition.
18in (46cm)   **$450—500**

Cloth Black Doll: Ca. 1910. American-made cloth doll with black face, painted, printed or embroidered features; jointed arms and legs; original clothes; all in good condition.

Mammy-type	**$ 250 up***
Babyland Rag-type, 13—15in (33—38cm), painted face	**750—850**
Stockinette (so-called Beecher-type)	**1800—2500**
1930s Mammy, 14—16in (36—41cm)	**150 up***
WPA, molded cloth face, 22in (56cm)	**1250**
Paint over molded stockinette (Chase-type)	**1500—1800**

*Greatly depending upon appeal.

21in (53cm) black stockinette doll, white paper eyes with painted lashes and shoe-button eyes, curly mohair wig. *Betty Harms Collection.*

18in (46cm) black painted stockinette doll, pierced nose. *Betty Harms Collection.*

Black Dolls continued

Black Composition Doll: Ca. 1920—on. German made character doll, all-composition, jointed at neck, shoulders and hips; molded hair or wig, glass eyes (sometimes flirty); appropriate clothes; all in good condition.

14in (36cm)   **$500**
18—20in (46—51cm)   **625—700**
31in (79cm)   **900—1000****

**Not enough price samples to compute a reliable range.

Black Composition Doll: Ca. 1930. American-made bent-limb baby or mama-type body, jointed at hips, shoulders and perhaps neck; molded hair, painted or sleep eyes; original or appropriate clothes; some have three yarn tufts of hair on either side and on top of the head; all in good condition.

Baby,
  10—12in (25—31cm)$ **75—95**
  16—17in (41—43cm) **150—165**
Mama Doll,
  20—22in (51—56cm) **150—175**
Patsy-type,
  10in (25cm)   **110—135**

31in (79cm) F.S. & Co. composition toddler with cloth torso and flirty eyes. *Leone McMullen Collection.*

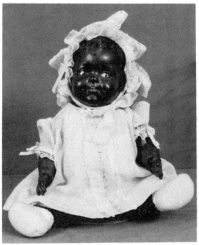

17in (43cm) black composition "Topsy -A Reliable Doll." *H&J Foulke, Inc.*

10in (25cm) black composition Patsy-type, all original. *Leone McMullen Collection.*

George Borgfeldt & Co.

Maker: George Borgfeldt, New York, N.Y., U.S.A., importer, assembler and distributor contracted with various doll factories, particularly in Germany and Japan, to make dolls and doll parts of all types and materials.

G.B. Character Baby: Ca. 1910. Perfect bisque head with smiling face, sleeping eyes, open mouth with teeth, human hair or mohair wig; composition baby body; appropriate clothing. All in good condition.

MARK:

Germany
G. B.

23—25in (58—64cm)   **$750—850**

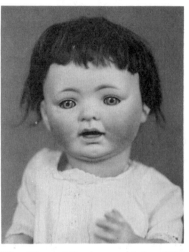

20in (51cm) G.B. character baby. *H&J Foulke, Inc.*

Lenci-Type Art Doll: My Playmate line. Pressed cardboard head covered with flocking, beautifully painted side-glancing eyes, closed mouth, mohair wig; cloth body with jointed limbs; original felt clothing. Very good condition.

14in (36cm)   **$350—450****
MIB   **550****

**Not enough price samples to compute a reliable range.

14in (36cm) *My Playmate* received by original owner in 1917. *Courtesy of Carolyn Guzzio.*

Boudoir Dolls

Maker: Various French, U.S. and Italian firms
Date: Early 1920s into the 1940s
Material: Heads of composition and other materials; bodies mostly cloth but also of composition and other substances
Size: Many 24—36in (61—91cm); some smaller
Mark: Mostly unmarked

Boudoir Doll: Head of composition, cloth or other material, painted features, mohair wig, composition or cloth stuffed body, unusually long extremities, usually high heeled shoes; original clothes elaborately designed and trimmed; all in good condition.

1920s Art Doll, exceptional quality, silk hair, 28—30in (71—76cm)	**$325—400**
Standard quality, dressed, 28—30in (71—76cm)	**95—115**
undressed	**50—55**
1940s composition head	**55—75**
Lenci, 24—28in (61—71cm)	**1200 up**

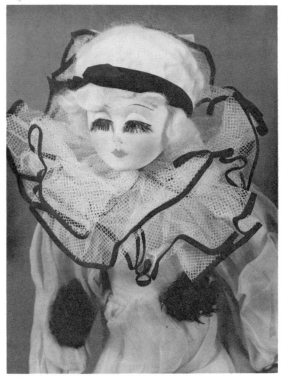

30in (76cm) boudoir doll with cloth face, all original. *Esther Schwartz Collection.*

Bru

Maker: Bru Jne. & Cie, Paris, France
Date: 1866—1899

Marked Brevete Bébé: Ca. 1870s. Perfect bisque swivel head on shoulder plate, cork pate, skin wig, paperweight eyes with shading on upper lid, closed mouth with white space between lips, full cheeks, pierced ears; gusseted kid body pulled high on shoulder plate and straight cut with bisque lower arms (no rivet joints); dressed; all in good condition. (For photograph see *6th Blue Book*, page 78.)

MARK: Size number only on head.
Oval sticker on body:

> BÉBÉ
> (Breveté SGDG
> PARIS)

13—14in (33—36cm)	$ 7000—8000	
17—18in (43—46cm)	10,000—12,000	

Fashion Lady: 1866—on. Perfect bisque swivel head on shoulder plate, cork pate, appropriate old wig, closed smiling mouth, paperweight eyes, pierced ears; gusseted kid lady body; original or appropriate old clothes; all in good condition. Incised with letters A through O in sizes 11in (28cm) to 36in (91cm) tall.

12—13in (31—33cm)	$ 2100—2400*
15in (38cm)	2600—3100*
17—18in (43—46cm)	3200—3700*
29in (74cm)	5500—6000
36in (91cm)	7250 up
Wood Body,	
19in (48cm)	4800—5500
Portrait Lady	
Duchess of Marlborough	
22in (56cm)	**23,100**

*Allow $800 extra for wood arms.

16in (41cm) smiling Bru fashion lady incised "D." (See color photograph on page 71.) *Yvonne Baird Collection.*

Bru continued

Marked Crescent or Circle Dot Bébé: Ca. late 1870s. Perfect bisque swivel head on a deep shoulder plate with molded breasts, cork pate, attractive wig, paperweight eyes, closed mouth with slightly parted lips, molded and painted teeth, plump cheeks, pierced ears; gusseted kid body with bisque lower arms (no rivet joints); dressed; all in good condition.

MARK: ⌐ ⊙

Sometimes with "BRU J^{ne}"

16—17in (41—43cm)	**$10,000—11,000**
21—22in (53—56cm)	**15,000—18,000**

21in (53cm) Circle Dot Bru Bébé. (See color photograph on page 70.) *Private Collection.*

Marked Nursing Bru (Bébé Teteur): 1878—1898. Perfect bisque head, shoulder plate and lower arms, kid body; upper arms and upper legs of metal covered with kid, lower legs of carved wood, or jointed composition body; attractive wig, lovely glass eyes, open mouth with hole for nipple, mechanism in head sucks up liquid, operates by turning key; nicely clothed; all in good condition. (For photograph see *7th Blue.Book*, page 88.)

13—15in (33—38cm) **$5200—6200**

Bru continued

Marked Bru Jne Bébé: Ca. 1880s. Perfect bisque swivel head on deep shoulder plate with molded breasts, cork pate, attractive wig, paperweight eyes, closed mouth, pierced ears; gusseted kid body with scalloped edge at shoulder plate, bisque lower arms with lovely hands, kid over wood upper arms, hinged elbow, all kid or wood lower legs (sometimes on a jointed composition body); dressed; all in good condition. (For body photograph see *6th Blue Book*, page 79.)

MARK: "BRU Jⁿᵉ"

Body Label:

> ♥ BÉBÉ BRU ᴮᵀᴱ S.G.D.G.
> Tout Contrefacteur sera saisiet poursuivi
> conformement ala Loi

15—17in (38—43cm)	**$ 8500—9500**
21—23in (53—58cm)	**12,500—16,500**
28—29in (71—74cm)	**20,000—23,500**
32in (81cm)	**27,000—30,000**

Marked Bru Jne R Bébé: Ca. Early 1890s. Perfect bisque head on a jointed composition body; attractive wig, paperweight eyes, closed mouth, pierced ears; dressed all in good condition.

MARK: BRU Jⁿᵉ R
11

Body Stamp: "Bebe Bru" with size number

14—16in (36—41cm)	**$4500—5000***
23—24in (58—61cm)	**6500—7500***
Open mouth	
22—24in (56—61cm)	**4500—5000***

*Allow more for an especially pretty model.

17in (43cm) Bru Jne Bébé. *Private Collection.*

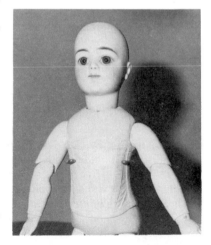

15in (38cm) Bru Jne R Bébé. *Crandall Collection.*

Brückner Rag Doll

Maker: Albert Brückner, Jersey City, N.J., U.S.A.
Date: 1901—on
Material: All-cloth with stiffened mask face
Size: 12—14in (31—36cm)
Mark: On right front shoulder: PAT'D. JULY 8ᵀᴴ 1901

Marked Brückner: Cloth head with printed features on stiffened mask face, cloth body flexible at shoulders and hips; appropriate clothes; all in good condition. These dolls were sold by Horsman as part of their "Babyland Rag" line.

12—14in (31—36cm)

White*	**$185—210**
Black	**200—250**
Topsy Turvy+	**350—400**
Dollypop	**200—250****

**Not enough price samples to compute a reliable range.

*For photograph see *7th Blue Book*, page 90.
+For photograph see *6th Blue Book*, page 80.

14in (36cm) Brückner black doll, all original. *Yvonne Baird Collection.*

Bye-Lo Baby

Maker: Bisque heads — J. D. Kestner; Alt, Beck & Gottschalck; Kling & Co.;
Hertel Schwab & Co.; all of Thüringia, Germany.
Composition heads — Cameo Doll Co., New York, N.Y., U.S.A.
Celluloid heads — Karl Standfuss, Saxony, Germany
Wooden heads (unauthorized) — Schoenhut of Philadelphia, PA.,
U.S.A.
All-Bisque Baby — J. D. Kestner
Cloth Bodies and Assembly — K & K Toy Co., New York, N.Y.,
U.S.A.
Date: 1922—on
Designer: Grace Storey Putnam
Distributor: George Borgfeldt, New York, N.Y., U.S.A.

Bisque Head Bye-Lo Baby: Ca. 1923. Perfect bisque head, cloth body with
curved legs (sometimes with straight legs), composition or celluloid hands;
sleep eyes; dressed. Made in seven sizes 9—20in (23—51cm). (May have
purple "Bye-Lo Baby" stamp on front of body.) Sometimes Mold ***#1373***
(ABG)

MARK: © 1923 *by*
Grace S. Putnam
MADE IN GERMANY

Head circumference:	
8—9in (20—23cm)	$ 350—375*
10in (25cm)	400—425*
12—13in (31—33cm)	475—550*
15in (38cm)	800*
17in (43cm)	1000—1100*
18in (46cm)	1250—1500*
Black, 13in (33cm)	2600*
10½in (27cm) with original basket, clothing and accessories	1400*
*Allow extra for original tagged gown and button.	
Mold ***#1369*** (ABG) socket head on composition body, 13—14in (33—36cm) long	1200—1300
Composition head, 1924. 12—13in (31—33cm) H.C.	350—375
Celluloid head, 10in (25cm) H.C.	350—400
Painted bisque head, late 1920s. 12—13in (31—33cm) H.C.	325—375
Wooden head, (Schoenhut), 1925.	1400—1600
Poured wax head (pink sateen or white cloth body), 15in (38cm) H.C.	3000—3500

Cameo Doll Company

Maker: Cameo Doll Company, New York, N.Y., U.S.A.; later Port Allegany, P.A., U.S.A. Original owner: Joseph L. Kallus.

Date: 1922—on

Material: Wood-pulp composition and wood

(See also *Kewpie* and *Baby Bo Kaye*)

Scootles: 1925. Designed by Rose O'Neill. All-composition, unmarked, jointed at neck, shoulders and hips; molded hair, blue or brown painted eyes looking to the side, closed smiling mouth; not dressed; all in very good condition. (For photograph see *7th Blue Book*, page 94.)

MARK: Wrist tag only

7—8in (18—20cm) all original, mint condition, wrist tag	**$600***	
12in (31cm)	**375**	
15—16in (38—41cm)	**450—475**	
Black, 14in (36cm)	**550—650****	

*One-time auction price.

**Not enough price samples to compute a reliable range.

Composition Little Annie Rooney: 1925. Designed by Jack Collins. All-composition, jointed at neck, shoulders and hips, legs as black stockings, feet with molded shoes; braided yarn wig, painted round eyes, watermelon mouth; original clothes; all in good condition.

MARK: None

16in (41cm) **$650****

**Not enough price samples to compute a reliable range.

Cameo Doll Company continued

Wood Segmented Characters: Designed by Joseph L. Kallus. Composition head, molded hair, painted features; segmented wood body; undressed; all in very good condition.

MARK: Label with name on chest.

Margie, 1929. 10in (25cm)	**$ 225—250**
Pinkie, 1930. 10in (25cm)	**275—325**
Joy, 1932. 10in (5cm)	**275—325**
15in (38cm)	**375—425**
Betty Boop, 1932. 12in (31cm)	**450—500**
Mint condition	**1000***

With molded bathing suit and composition legs; wearing a cotton print dress, (For photograph see *5th Blue Book*, page 82.)

12in (31cm)	**650**
Bimbo, 1932. 9in (23cm)	**250****

*One-time auction price.

**Not enough price samples to compute a reliable range.

10in (25cm) *Margie* variant with unusual red torso, upper arms and feet. For a more commonly found version of *Margie* see *7th Blue Book*, page 95. *H&J Foulke, Inc.*

10in (25cm) *Pinkie*. *H&J Foulke, Inc.*

Cameo Doll Company continued

15in (38cm) *Joy*. *H&J Foulke, Inc.*

9in (23cm) **Bimbo**. *Miriam Blankman Collection.*

Giggles: 1946. Designed by Rose O'Neill. All-composition, unmarked, jointed at neck, shoulders and hips, molded hair with bun in back, large painted side-glancing eyes, closed mouth; original romper; all in very good condition. (For photograph see *5th Blue Book*, page 83.)
MARK: Paper wrist tag only
14in (36cm) **$450—475**

Campbell Kid

Maker: E. I. Horsman Co., Inc., New York, N.Y., U.S.A.; American Character Doll Co., New York, N.Y., U.S.A.
Date: 1910—on
Material: Composition head and arms, cloth body and legs; or all-composition
Size: Usually 9—16in (23-41cm)
Designer: Grace G. Drayton

Campbell Kid: 1910-1914. By Horsman. Marked composition head with flange neck, molded and painted bobbed hair, painted round eyes to the side, watermelon mouth; original cloth body, composition arms, cloth legs and feet; original romper suit; all in fair condition. (For photograph see *7th Blue Book*, page 97.)
MARK: On head: E.I.H. © 1910

Cloth label on sleeve:

> The Campbell Kids
> Trademark by
> Joseph Campbell
> Mfg. by E. I. HORSMAN Co.

10—13in (25—33cm) **$150—175**

Campbell Kid: 1928. By American Character, sometimes called "Dolly Dingle". All-composition with swivel head, jointed shoulders and hips; molded and painted hair, eyes to the side, watermelon mouth; original clothes; all in good condition. (For photograph see *4th Blue Book*, page 86.)
MARK: On back:
"A PETITE DOLL"
12in (31cm) **$450—500****

**Not enough price samples to compute a reliable range.

Campbell Kid: 1948. By Horsman. Unmarked all-composition, molded painted hair, painted eyes to the side, watermelon mouth; painted white socks and black slippers; original clothes; all in good condition.
12in (31cm) **$250—275**

12in (31cm) *Campbell Kid*, 1948, all original. *Betty Harms Collection.*

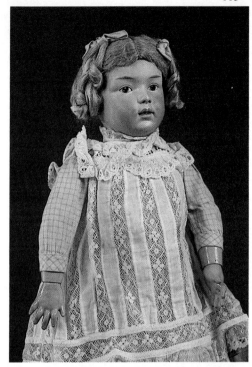

RIGHT: 17in (43cm) Gebrüder Heubach 7407 pouty character child. For further information see page 222. *Yvonne Baird Collection.*

BELOW LEFT: 7in (18cm) Gebrüder Heubach 9594 googly. For further information see page 205. *H&J Foulke, Inc.*

BELOW RIGHT: 7½in (19cm) all-bisque Gebrüder Heubach character boy. For further information see page 225. *H&J Foulke, Inc.*

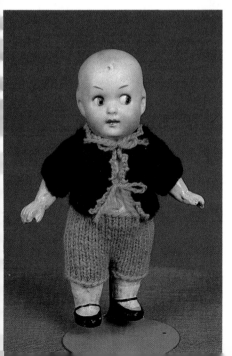

17in (43cm) Italian hard plastic child, all original. For further information see page 240. *H&J Foulke, Inc.*

Rare boxed set of 3 Royal Handmaidens, Traditional Japanese *Hina Matsuri* or Girls' Day Dolls. For further information see page 321. *Betty Lunz Collection.*

LEFT: 14in (36cm) Jumeau incised "E 5 J." For further information see page 245. *Yvonne Baird Collection.* **RIGHT:** 18in (46cm) Jumeau fashion lady, all original. For further information see page 243. *Yvonne Baird Collection.*

RIGHT: 22in (56cm) 1907 stamped in red "Tête Jumeau." For further information see page 247. *Private Collection.*

BELOW: 23½ in (60cm) early so-called almond-eyed or portrait Jumeau. For further information see page 244. *Yvonne Baird Collection.*

Triste or long-face Jumeau. For further information see page 244. *Yvonne Baird Collection.*

19in (48cm) cloth **Kamkins**, all original. For further information see page 249. *Private Collection.*

20in (51cm) K&K character baby. For further information see page 248. *H&J Foulke, Inc.*

16in (41cm) Kämmer & Reinhardt 114 pouty character child. For further information see page 255. *Yvonne Baird Collection.*

7in (18cm) J.D. Kestner 133 child. For further information see page 261. *H&J Foulke, Inc.*

21in (53cm) Kestner 262 character baby for Catterfelder Puppenfabrik. For further information see page 121. *H&J Foulke, Inc.*

25in (64cm) J. D. Kestner 143 character child. For further information see page 262. *Joanna Ott Collection.*

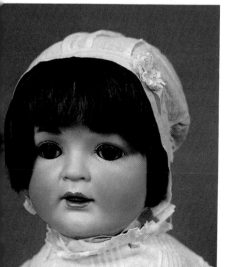

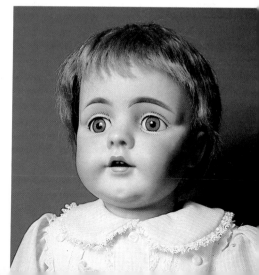

12in (31cm) Swiss wood boy with lightly carved hair. For further information see page 396. *H&J Foulke, Inc.*

21in (53cm) J.D. Kestner 172 ***Gibson Girl***. For further information see page 266. *Mary Lou Rubright Collection.*

11in (28cm) J.D. Kestner child with closed mouth incised "5." For further information see page 258. *Private Collection.*

Catterfelder Puppenfabrik

Maker: Catterfelder Puppenfabrik, Catterfeld, Thüringia, Germany
Heads by J. D. Kestner and other porcelain makers
Date: 1902—on
Material: Bisque head; composition body *C. P.*
Trademark: My Sunshine
Mark:

C.P. Child Doll: Ca. 1902—on. Perfect bisque head, good wig, sleep eyes, open mouth with teeth; composition jointed body; dressed; all in good condition.

#264 (made by Kestner)

17—18in (43—46cm)	**$500—550**
22—24in (56—61cm)	**650—750**

C.P. Character Child: Ca. 1910—on. Perfect bisque character face with wig, painted eyes; composition jointed body; dressed; all in good condition. Sometimes mold *#207.* (For photograph see *5th Blue Book*, page 85.)

15in—16in (38cm)	**$2650—2850****

**Not enough price samples to compute a reliable range.

C.P. Character Baby: Ca. 1910—on. Perfect bisque character face with wig or molded hair, painted or glass eyes; jointed baby body; dressed; all in good condition.

#200, 201, 208, 209, 262, 263

15—17in (38—43cm)	**$450—500**
22—24in (56—61cm)	**750—850**

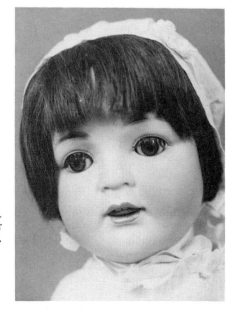

21in (53cm) 262 character baby with J.D. Kestner mark made for C.P. For color photograph see page 119. *H&J Foulke, Inc.*

Celluloid Dolls

Makers: Germany:
Rheinische Gummi und Celluloid Fabric Co. (Turtle symbol)
Buschow & Beck. *Minerva* trademark. (Helmet symbol)
E. Maar & Sohn. *Emasco* trademark. (3 M symbol)
Cellba. (Mermaid symbol)
Poland:
P.R. Zask. (ASK in triangle)
France:
Petitcolin. (Eagle symbol)
Société Nobel Francaise. (SNF in diamond)
Neumann & Marx. (Dragon symbol)
Société Industrielle de Celluloid (Sicoine)
United States:
Parsons-Jackson Co., Cleveland, Ohio and other companies
Date: 1895—1940s
Material: All-celluloid or celluloid head with jointed kid, cloth or composition body.
Marks: **Various as indicated above: sometimes also in combination with the** marks of J.D. Kestner, Kämmer & Reinhardt, Bruno Schmidt, Käthe Kruse and König & Wernicke.

Celluloid head Child doll: Ca. 1900—on. Molded hair or wig, painted or glass eyes, open or closed mouth; cloth or kid body, celluloid or composition arms; dressed; all in good condition.

Painted eyes:
13—15in (33—38cm)**$110—135**
13—14in (33—36cm)
Tommy Tucker-type character **110—125**
Glass eyes:
13—15in (33—38cm) **150—175**
18—20in (46—51cm) **200—225**
22—24in (56—61cm) **250—275**

All-Celluloid Child Doll: Ca. 1900—on. Jointed at neck, shoulders, and hips; molded hair or wig, painted eyes; dressed; all in good condition.
6—7in (13—15cm) **$ 35—45**
9—10in (23—25cm) **80—90**
13—14in (33—36cm) **125—150**

Glass eyes:
12—13in (31—33cm) **165—185***
15—16in (38—41cm) **225—275***
18in (46cm) **325—375***
Parsons-Jackson toddler
with stork trademark,
13in (33cm) **225—250**
*Allow extra for K★R dolls and character faces.

15in (38cm) all-celluloid child with turtle mark, glass eyes, all original. *H&J Foulke, Inc.*

Celluloid Dolls continued

13in (33cm) all-celluloid Parsons-Jackson toddler with stork trademark. *H&J Foulke, Inc.*

Celluloid socket head Child Doll: Ca. 1910—on. Wig, glass eyes, sometimes flirty, open mouth with teeth; ball-jointed or bent-limb composition body; dressed; all in good condition.

15—18in (38—46cm)	**$250—300**
22—24in (56—61cm)	**400—450**

***Characters*:**
K★R 701,

12—13in (31—33cm)	**700—750**

K★R 717,

16in (41cm) flirty	**350—375**

K★R 728,
12—13in (31—33cm)

baby	**300—350**

K&W toddler,

16in (41cm)	**350—375**

12in (31cm) K★R 701 character child. *Dolly Valk Collection.*

All-Celluloid Baby: Ca. 1910—on. Bent-limb baby, molded hair, painted eyes, closed mouth; jointed arms and/or legs; no clothes; all in good condition.

6—8in (15—20cm)	**$ 60—80**
10—12in (25—31cm)	**90—115**
15in (38cm)	**135**
Japanese, 18—20in (46—51cm)	**175—225**
Black, French SNF, 19in (48cm)	**250—300**
Glass eyes, 14—15in (36—38cm)	**165—185**

12in (31cm) All-celluloid baby with skin wig, made in U.S.A. *Dolly Valk Collection.*

Century Doll Co.

Maker: Century Doll Co., New York, N.Y., U.S.A.; bisque heads by J.D. Kestner, Germany

Date: 1909—on

Material: Bisque or composition head, cloth body, composition arms (and legs)

Mark: "Century Doll Co." Sometimes ⟨K⟩ (for Kestner). "Germany"

Marked Century Infant: Ca. 1925. Perfect bisque solid-dome head, molded and painted hair, sleep eyes, open/closed mouth; cloth body, composition hands or limbs; dressed; all in good condition. (See photographs in *Kestner, King of Dollmakers*, pages 193 and 194.)

Head circumference:

10—11in (25—28cm)	**$475—525**
13—14in (33—36cm)	**650—700**

Mama doll, bisque shoulder head #281, (See photograph in *Kestner, King of Dollmakers,* page 194.) 21in (53cm)   **650—700****

**Not enough price samples to compute a reliable average.

Chuckles. 1927 composition shoulder head with character face, molded hair, smiling open mouth with 2 teeth, dimples, tin sleep eyes. Cloth torso with cryer, composition arms and legs; appropriate clothing. All in good condition.

Mark: Chuckles
Century
Dolls
16½in (42cm)   **150—165**

16½in (42cm) *Chuckles. H&J Foulke, Inc.*

Chad Valley

Maker: Chad Valley Co. (formerly Johnson Bros., Ltd.), Birmingham, England
Date: 1917—on
Material: All-cloth
Mark: Cloth label usually on foot:

"HYGENIC TOYS
Made in England by
CHAD VALLEY CO. LTD."

Cardboard tag:

"The
'Mabel Lucie Attwell'
Doll
Regd & Patented   or
Sole Makers
Chad Valley
Co. Ltd."

"THE
CHAD VALLEY
HYGENIC
TEXTILE
TOYS
Made in England"

Chad Valley Doll: All-cloth, usually felt face and velvet body, jointed neck, shoulders and hips; mohair wig, glass or painted eyes; original clothes; all in excellent condition.

Characters, painted eyes,
  10—12in (25cm) **$ 65—95**
Children, painted eyes,
  9in (23cm)   **125**
  13—14in (33—36cm) **300—350**
  16—18in (41—46cm) **400—500**
Children, glass eyes,
  16—18in (41—46cm) **550—650**
Royal Children, glass eyes
  16—18in (41—46cm) **1200—1500**
Mabel Lucie Attwell, glass inset side-glancing eyes, smiling watermelon mouth. (For photograph see *6th Blue Book*, page 63.)
  14in (36cm)   **500—550**
Snow White and Seven Dwarfs
  7 & 13in (18 & 33cm)
  complete set   **1500—1700**

See color photograph on page 71.

18in (46cm) *Scots Boy* with glass eyes, all original. *H&J Foulke, Inc.*

Martha Chase

Maker: Martha Jenks Chase, Pawtucket, R.I., U.S.A.

Date: 1889—on

Material: Stockinette and cloth, painted in oils; some fully painted washable models; some designed for hospital training use.

PAWTUCKET, R.I
MADE IN U.S.A.

Size: 9in (23cm) to life-size

Designer: Martha Jenks Chase

Mark: "Chase Stockinet Doll" stamp on left leg or under left arm, paper label on back (usually gone)

Chase Doll: Head and limbs of stockinette, treated and painted with oils, large painted eyes with thick upper lashes, rough-stroked hair to provide texture, cloth bodies jointed at shoulders, hips, elbows and knees, later ones only at shoulders and hips; some bodies completely treated; showing wear.

Baby,

13—15in (33—38cm)	**$ 425—500**
17—21in (43—53cm)	**600—700**
24—26in (61—66cm)	**800—850**
37—40in (94—102cm)	**1800**

Child, molded bobbed hair. (For photograph see *6th Blue Book*, page 95.)   15—17in (38—43cm) — **800—900**

Lady, (For photograph see *5th Blue Book*, page 91.)
15in (38cm) — **1300—1500**

Black, 24in (61cm) — **5500**

20in (51cm) Chase baby. *H&J Foulke, Inc.*

24in (61cm) Black chase lady. *Yvonne Baird Collection.*

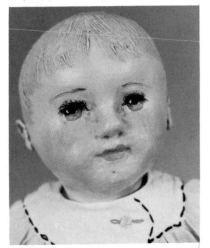

China Heads
(German)

Maker: Firms such as Kling & Co., Alt, Beck & Gottschalck, Kestner & Co., Hertwig & Co. and others
Material: China head, cloth or kid body, leather arms or china limbs
Mark: Usually unmarked, sometimes marked with numbers and/or "Germany"

Bald (so-called Biedermeier): Ca. 1840-1860. China shoulder head with bald head, some with black areas on top of head, proper wig, blue painted eyes; cloth body, bisque, china or leather arms; nicely dressed; all in good condition. (For photograph see *7th Blue Book*, page 113.)
Fine quality,
15—17in (38—43cm) $ **850—950**
22—24in (56—61cm) **1300—1500**
Standard quality,
15—18in (38—46cm) **400—500**
24in (61cm) **750—775**
Glass eyes, fine quality,
25in (64cm) **2850**

Wood-Body: Ca. 1840. Head with early hair style mounted on a peg-wooden body; usually with china lower limbs; undressed; in good condition. (For photograph see *5th Blue Book*, page 98.)
Covered Wagon hairdo,
6—7in (15—18cm) $ **900—1100**
15—17in (38—43cm) **1900—2100**
Unusual hairdo,
15—17in (38—43cm) **2600—2900**

Early Style: Ca. 1840s. Black-haired china shoulder head may have pink tint; old cloth body; dressed; all in good condition.
Bun,
6in (15cm) $ **600**
18—21in (46—53cm) **1500—3800***
Brown hair. (For photograph see *5th Blue Book*, page 93.)
18in (46cm) **3500 up**
Long curls,
10in (25cm) **800—900**
16in (41cm) falling onto shoulder **2250****
*Depending upon quality, hairdo and rarity.

10½in (27cm) early china head with pink tint, long curls. *H&J Foulke, Inc.*

**Not enough price samples to compute a reliable range.

China Heads (German) continued

Brown Eyes: Ca. 1850. Black hair parted in center, smooth to the head; cloth body with leather or china arms; dressed; all in good condition.

MARK: None

Greiner-style. (For photograph see *6th Blue Book*, page 97.)
   17—19in (43—48cm)   **$800—1000**

Waves framing face. (For photograph see *7th Blue Book*, page 114.)
   *17—19in (43—48cm)   **550—650**

Covered Wagon style,
   18—21in (46—53cm)   **900—1100**

Child, Motschmann-type with swivel neck: Ca. 1850. China head and flange neck with shoulder plate, midsection and lower limbs of china; black painted hair, blue painted eyes; with or without clothes; all in good condition. (For photograph see *4th Blue Book*, page 97.)

MARK: None
10—12in (25—31cm)**$1650—1750**

Glass Eyes: Ca. 1850. Black-haired china shoulder head with hair parted in middle and styled very close to head, dark glass eyes; cloth body with leather arms; appropriate clothes; all in good condition. (For photograph see *6th Blue Book*, page 100.)

MARK: None
16—18in (41—46cm)**$2250—2550**

19in (48cm) pink tint china head with brown eyes, all original. See color photograph on page 72. *Yvonne Baird Collection.*

Fancy Hairdo: Ca. 1860. China shoulder head with black hair, brush marks, elaborate style with braids, wings, ornaments, blue painted eyes; old cloth body; appropriate clothes; all in good condition.

18—21in (46—53cm)$ **850 up***
So-called *Jenny Lind* style,
23in (58cm)   **1250**
*Depending upon quality, hairdo and rarity.

TOP LEFT: 18½in (47cm) china head lady with fancy molded and braided bun. *Yvonne Baird Collection.*

8in (20cm) early pink tint china head with short hair, generally used as a man, but in this case possibly a child, apparently all original. *H&J Foulke, Inc.*

Man: Ca. 1850. Black-haired china shoulder head with short hair, blue painted eyes, cloth body; appropriate clothes; all in good condition. (For photograph see also *6th Blue Book*, page 101.)
MARK: None
Fine quality with brush marks around face (may have pink tint),
8in 22in (46—56cm)$ **450—500**
20in (51cm)   **1500 up**
Standard quality,
18—20in (46—51cm)   **500—600**

Covered Wagon (so-called): 1850—1870. Black-haired china shoulder head with pink tint, hair parted in middle and close to head with vertical sausage curls; old cloth body with varied extremities; well dressed; all in good condition.

MARK: None
10—13in (25—33cm) **$300—350**
16—18in (41—46cm)   **475—525**
22—24in (56—61cm)   **625—700**
Brown eyes,
18—21in (46—53cm) **900—1100**

Curly Top (so-called): Ca. 1860. Black- or blonde-haired shoulder head with distinctive large horizontal curls around forehead and face; old cloth body with leather arms or china arms and legs; nicely dressed; all in good condition. (For photograph see *7th Blue Book*, page 115.)
MARK: None
15—18in (38—46cm) **$500—600**

China Heads (German) continued

Pierced Ears: Ca. 1860. China shoulder head with black hair styled with curls on forehead and pulled back to curls on lower back of head, blue painted eyes, pierced ears; original cloth body with leather arms or china arms and legs; appropriate clothes; all in good condition. (For photograph see *5th Blue Book*, page 97.)

MARK: None

18—22in (46—56cm) **$850 up***

Ordinary hair style,

15—16in (38—41cm) **500—550**

*Depending upon quality and rarity of hairdo.

Snood: Ca. 1860. China shoulder head with black painted hair, slender features, blue painted eyes, molded eyelids, molded snood on hair; cloth body with leather arms or china limbs; appropriate clothes; all in good condition.

MARK: None

18—22in (46—56cm) **$ 650 up***

Grape Lady,

19—21in (48—53cm) **1350—1500**

Countess Dagmar,

18in (46cm) **750—800**

Blonde hair, black snood, pink ribbon,

16—18in (41—46cm) **850—950**

*Depending upon quality and rarity of hairdo.

16in (41cm) china head with molded snood and ribbons. *Yvonne Baird Collection.*

20in (51cm) china head *Grape Lady* with fancy molded snood. *Joe Jackson and Joel Pearson.*

China Heads (German) continued

Flat Top (so-called): Ca. 1860-1870. China shoulder head with black hair parted in middle, smooth on top with short curls, blue painted eyes; old cloth body, extremities of leather or china; appropriate clothes; all in good condition.

MARK: None

5½in (14cm) china head with flat-top hairdo. *H&J Foulke, Inc.*

5—6in (13—15cm)	$ 85—95
14—16in (36—41cm)	175—200
20—22in (51—56cm)	250—300
24—26in (61—66cm)	350—400
Swivel neck, 15in (38cm)	650—700**

**Not enough price samples to compute a reliable range.

20in (51cm) modified flat-top hairdo with rounded crown. *H&J Foulke, Inc.*

High Brow (so-called): Ca. 1860-1870. China shoulder head with black painted hair, high forehead, center part, smooth top, curls clustered above ears; cloth body, china arms; dressed; all in good condition.

14—16in (36—41cm)	$200—225
20—22in (51—56cm)	325—375
24—26in (61—66cm)	450—500
Molded necklace, 24in (61cm)	600—650

Adelina Patti (so-called): Ca. 1870. Black-haired china shoulder head with high forehead, white center part with wings on each side, short overall curls, brush marks at temple; cloth body with leather arms or china arms and legs. (For photograph see *7th Blue Book*, page 117.)

MARK: None

11—13in (28—33cm)	$225—250
21—24in (53—61cm)	450—550

25in (64cm) china head with high brow hairdo. *H&J Foulke, Inc.*

China Heads (German) continued

Spill Curl: Ca. 1870. China shoulder head with café-au-lait or black painted hair, massed curls on top spilling down back and sides onto shoulders, brush marks around the forehead and temples, exposed ears; cloth body with china arms and legs; appropriate clothes; all in good condition. (For photograph see *5th Blue Book*, page 98.)

20—23in (51—58cm) **$600—650**

Dolley Madison (so-called): 1875-1895. Black-haired china shoulder head with molded ribbon bow in front and molded band on back of head, blue painted eyes; old cloth body with leather arms; nicely dressed; in good condition.

MARK: None

18—21in (46—51cm) **$400—450**

19in (48cm) china head with Dolley Madison hairdo. *H&J Foulke, Inc.*

Bangs: Ca. 1880. Black- or blonde-haired china shoulder head with bangs on forehead; cloth body with china arms and legs to kid body; dressed; all in good condition.

MARK: Some marked with A.B.G. Mold numbers (see page 54.)
or
Kling & Co:

9—11in (23—28cm) **$175—200**
15—18in (38—46cm) **275—300**
20—22in (51—56cm) **350—400**
25in (64cm) **450**

9½in (24cm) blonde china head with bangs, appears to be Mold **#1000** from Alt, Beck & Gottschalck. *H&J Foulke, Inc.*

China Heads (German) continued

Boy or Child: Ca. 1880s. Black-or blonde-haired china shoulder head with short wavy hair and exposed ears; cloth body with china limbs; dressed; all in good condition. Some are from Alt, Beck & Gottschalck #784.

14—16in (36—41cm) **$225—250**
20—23in (51—58cm) **325—375**

> 14in (36cm) china head boy or child, appears to be Alt, Beck & Gottschalck *#784. H&J Foulke, Inc.*

Common 1890s, or Low Brow Style: Ca. 1890s—on. Black or blonde wavy hair style on china shoulder head, blue painted eyes; old cloth or kid body with stub, leather, bisque or china limbs; appropriate clothes; all in good condition.

7—8in (18—20cm) **$ 65—75**
12—13in (31—33cm) **110—135**
15—17in (39—43cm) **160—175**
21—24in (53—61cm) **225—275**

> 18in (46cm) china head with common hairdo. *H&J Foulke, Inc.*

Pet Name: Ca. 1905. Made by Hertwig & Co. for Butler Bros., N.Y. China shoulder head, molded yoke with name in gold; black or blonde painted hair (one-third were blonde), blue painted eyes; old cloth body (some with alphabet or other figures printed on cotton material), china limbs; properly dressed; all in good condition. Used names such as *Agnes, Bertha, Daisy, Dorothy, Edith, Esther, Ethel, Florence, Helen, Mabel, Marion* and *Pauline*.

9—10in (23—25cm) **$125—140**
14—16in (36—41cm) **200—225**
19—21in (48—53cm) **275—300**

16½in (42cm) china head *Agnes* pet name. *H&J Foulke, Inc.*

Cloth, Printed

Maker: Various American companies, such as Cocheco Mfg Co., Lawrence & Co., Arnold Print Works, Art Fabric Mills and Selchow & Righter.

Date: 1896—on

Material: All-cloth

Size: 6—30in (15—76cm)

Mark: Mark could be found on fabric part which was discarded after cutting,

---

Cloth, Printed Doll: Face, hair, underclothes, shoes and socks printed on cloth; all in good condition, some soil acceptable. Dolls in printed underwear are sometimes found dressed in old petticoats and frocks. Names such as: ***Dolly Dear, Merry Marie, Improved Foot Doll, Standish No Break Doll,*** and so on.

6—7in (15—18cm)	**$ 75—85**
16—18in (41—46cm)	**150—165**
24—26in (61—66cm)	**185—210**
Uncut sheet, 20in (51cm) doll	**200—250**

Brownies: 1892.

Designed by Palmer Cox; marked on foot.

8in (20cm)	**85—95**
12 dolls on 2 uncut sheets	**1000**

Boys and Girls with printed outer clothes, Ca. 1903,

12—13in (31—33cm)	**160—185**

Darkey Doll,

16in (41cm)	**175—200**

Aunt Jemima Family

(four dolls)	**85 each**
Punch & Judy	**425 pair**

George and Martha Washington Family,

Art Fabric, 1901, Sheet of four uncut dolls **650**

Gutsell, 16in (41cm) **275**

Black Child, Art Fabric,

18in (46cm)	**400—450**

See color photograph on page 73.

17in (43cm) ***Improved Foot Doll.*** *H&J Foulke, Inc.*

18in (46cm) Art Fabric black children. *Yvonne Baird Collection.*

Cloth, Russian

Maker: Unknown craftsmen
Date: Ca. 1930
Material: All-cloth
Size: 10—15in (25—38cm)
Mark: "Made in Soviet Union" sometimes with identification of doll, such as
"Ukranian Woman", "Village Boy", "Smolensk District Woman"

Russian Cloth Doll: All-cloth with stockinette head and hands, molded face
with hand-painted features; authentic regional clothes; all in very good
condition.

11in (28cm) child	**$ 65—75**
15in (38cm)	**110—125**

15in (38cm) *Village Boy* and *Smolensk District Woman*, both all original. *H&J Foulke, Inc.*

Dewees Cochran

Maker: Dewees Cochran, Fenton, CA., U.S.A.
Date: 1940—on
Material: Latex
Size: 9—18in (23—46cm)
Designer: Dewees Cochran
Mark: Signed under arm or behind right ear

Dewees Cochran Doll: Latex with jointed neck, shoulders and hips; human hair wig, painted eyes, character face; dressed; all in good condition.
15—16in (38—41cm) ***Cindy,*** 1947-1948.   **$ 650—750**
Grow-up Dolls: Stormy, Angel, Bunnie, J.J. and ***Peter Ponsett***
each at ages 5, 7, 11, 16 and 20, 1952-1956.   **1000—1200**
Look-Alike Dolls (6 different faces)   **1000—1100**
Baby, 9in (23cm)   **1100—1300**
Individual Portrait Children   **1200—1400 up**
Composition American Children (See Effanbee, page 163.)

15in (38cm) ***Brother and Sister Portrait children***, all original. Esther Schwartz Collection.

Columbian Doll

Maker: Emma and Marietta Adams
Date: 1891—1910 or later
Material: All-cloth
Size: 15—29in (38—74cm)
Mark: Stamped on back of body
   Before 1900:

> "COLUMBIAN DOLL
> EMMA E. ADAMS
> OSWEGO CENTRE
> N.Y."

   After 1906:

> "THE COLUMBIAN DOLL
> MANUFACTURED BY
> MARIETTA ADAMS RUTTAN
> OSWEGO, N.Y."

Columbian Doll: All-cloth with hair and features hand-painted on a flat face; treated limbs; appropriate clothes; all in fair condition, showing wear. (Also see photograph in *7th Blue Book*, page 124.)
17—21in (43—53cm)   **$3100—3500**
Columbian type,
 18—20in (46—51cm)   **700—800**

15½in (39cm) *Colum-bian* doll, restored face. *Private Collection.*

Composition
(American)

Maker: Various United States firms, many unidentified
Date: 1912—on
Material: All-composition or composition head and cloth body, some with composition limbs

27in (69cm) early composition head character boy. *Yvonne Baird Collection.*

All-Composition Child Doll: 1912—1920. Various firms, such as Bester Doll Co., New Era Novelty Co., New Toy Mfg. Co., Superior Doll Mfg. Co., Colonial Toy Mfg. Co. Composition with mohair wig, sleep eyes, open mouth; ball-jointed composition body; appropriate clothes; all in good condition. These are patterned after German bisque head dolls. (For photographs see *7th Blue Book*, pages 56 and 144.)
22—24in (56-61cm)   **$250—275**

Early Composition Character Head: Ca. 1912. Composition head with molded hair and painted features; hard cloth body with composition hands; appropriate clothes; all in good condition.

10—11in (25—28cm)	**$ 90—110**
12—13in (31—33cm)	**125—150**
24—26in (61—66cm)	**350 up**

16in (41cm) *Mama doll*, all original. *H&J Foulke, Inc.*

Girl-type Mama Dolls: Ca. 1920—on. Made by various American companies. Composition head with hair wig, sleep eyes, open mouth with teeth; composition shoulder plate, arms and legs, cloth body; original clothes; all in good condition, of good quality.

16—18in (41—46cm)	**$140—175**
22—25in (56—64cm)	**200—250**

Composition (American) continued

Patsy-type Girl: Ca. 1930s. All-composition with molded bobbed hair, sleep or painted eyes, closed mouth; jointed at neck, shoulders and hips; original clothes; all in very good condition, of good quality.

9—10in (23—25cm)   **$ 90—110**
14—16in (36—41cm)   **160—185**
20in (51cm)   **225**

19½in (50cm) ***Patsy***-type doll, all original. *H&J Foulke, Inc.*

Composition Baby: Ca. 1930. All-composition or composition head, arms and legs, cloth torso; with molded and painted hair, sleep eyes; appropriate or original clothes; all in very good condition, of good quality.

10—12in (25—31cm)   **$ 75—95**
16—18in (41—46cm)   **135—160**
24in (61cm)   **250**

FAR RIGHT: 26in (66cm) unmarked composition baby, appropriate old clothes. *H&J Foulke, Inc.*

18in (46cm) ***Shirley Temple***-type doll, all original. *Private Collection.*

Dionne-type Doll: Ca. 1935. All-composition with molded hair or wig, sleep eyes (painted in small dolls), closed or open mouth; jointed at neck, shoulders and hips; original clothes; all in very good condition, of good quality. (For photograph see *6th Blue Book*, page 113.)

7—8in (18—20cm)   **$ 50—65**
18—20in (46—51cm)
   toddler   **175—225**

Shirley Temple-type Girl: Ca. 1935—on. All-composition, jointed at neck, shoulders and hips; blonde curly mohair wig, sleep eyes, open smiling mouth with teeth; original clothes; all in very good condition, of good quality.

16—18in (41—46cm)   **$175—200**

Composition (American) continued

Alexander-type Girl: Ca. 1935. All-composition, jointed at neck, shoulders and hips; sleeping eyes, mohair wig, closed mouth, dimples. Original or appropriate clothing. All in good condition, of good quality.

13in (33cm)   **$125—150**

Foreign Costume Doll: Ca. 1940. All-composition, jointed at neck, shoulders and hips, sleep or painted eyes, mohair wig, closed mouth; original costume; all in good condition.

11in (28cm)
Excellent quality   **$55—65**
Standard quality   **35—40**

Miscellaneous Specific Dolls:
Orphan Annie, 1920s.
12in (31cm)   **$150—175**
Jackie Robinson.
13½in (34cm)   **500**
Trudy 3 faces, 1946.
14in (36cm)   **175—200**

13in (33cm) *Alexander-type girl*, appropriate clothing. *H&J Foulke, Inc.*

11in (28cm) *Foreign Costume doll*, excellent quality, all original. *H&J Foulke, Inc.*

Composition
(German)

Maker: Various German firms, such as König & Wernicke, Kämmer & Reinhardt and others
Date: Ca. 1925
Material: All-composition or composition head and cloth body
Size: Various

All-Composition Child Doll: Socket head with good wig, sleep (sometimes flirty) eyes, open mouth with teeth; jointed composition body; appropriate clothes; all in good condition, of excellent quality. (For photograph see *6th Blue Book*, page 111.)

12—14in (31—36cm)	**$195—225**
18—20in (46—51cm)	**275—300**

Character face, (For photograph see *7th Blue Book*, page 128.)

18—20in (46—51cm)	**350—400**

Character Baby: Composition head with good wig, sleep eyes, open mouth with teeth; bent-limb composition baby body or hard-stuffed cloth body; appropriate clothes; all in good condition, of excellent quality.

All-composition baby,
16—18in (41—46cm)**$200—250**
Hard-stuffed cloth body,
20—23in (51—58cm) **250—300**
All-composition toddler,
16—18in (41—46cm) **275—325**

23in (58cm) German unmarked composition character baby, hard-stuffed cloth body. *H&J Foulke, Inc.*

Composition Shoulder Head
(Patent Washable Dolls)

Maker: Various German firms
Date: 1880—1915
Material: Composition shoulder head, cloth body, composition lower limbs
Size: 10—42in (25—107cm)
Mark: None

Composition Shoulder Head: Composition shoulder head with mohair or skin wig, glass eyes, closed or open mouth; cloth body with composition arms and lower legs, sometimes with molded boots; appropriately dressed; all in good condition.

Superior Quality:

13—15in (33—38cm)	**$275—325**
19—21in (48—53cm)	**400—450**
24in (61cm)	**500—550**
30in (76cm) mint condition, beautiful original clothes, auction price	**1000**
Swivel neck, 17in (43cm)	**500—550**

Painted hair,

9—10in (23—25cm)	**135—150**

Standard Quality:

11—12in (28—31cm)	**125—135**
14—16in (36—41cm)	**175—200**
18—20in (46—51cm)	**225—250**
22—24in (56—61cm)	**275—300**
30in (76cm)	**400—450**

8½in (22cm) composition shoulder head with painted hair. *H&J Foulke, Inc.*

18in (46cm) composition shoulder head with skin wig, possibly original clothing. *H&J Foulke, Inc.*

Creche Figures

Maker: Various European craftsmen, primarily Italian
Date: 18th and 19th centuries
Material: Wood and terra-cotta on a wire frame
Size: Various
Mark: None

Creche Figures of various people in a Christmas scene: 18th century. Gesso over wood head and limbs, fabric-covered wire frame body; beautifully detailed features with carved hair and glass inset eyes, lovely hands; original or appropriate replacement clothes; all in good condition.

13—14in (33—35cm) **$350—450***
18—20in (46—51cm) **750—850***

*Allow more for wood-jointed body.
6in (15cm)
wood-jointed body **275**

Mid 19th Century: Later doll with terra-cotta head and limbs, painted eyes; fabric-covered wire frame body; workmanship not as detailed; original or appropriate clothes; all in good condition.

11—13in (28—33cm) **$175—200**
15in (38cm) **225**
22in (56cm) **400—425**
*Price would be higher on "art" and "antiques" market.

16in (41cm) 18th century creche lady.
Private Collection.

Danel

Maker: Danel & Cie., Paris & Montreuil-sous-Bois, France
Date: 1889—1895
Material: Bisque socket head, composition body
Trademarks: Paris Bébé, Bébé Français (Also used by Jumeau)

Marked Paris Bébé: 1889. Perfect bisque socket head, good wig, paperweight eyes, closed mouth, pierced ears; composition jointed body; appropriately dressed; all in good condition.

Mark: On head   TÊTE DÉPOSÉ   On body
                PARIS BEBE

24—26in (61—66cm) **$4100—4500**

PARIS-BEBE
Breveté

See color photograph on page 193.

Marked B.F.: Ca. 1891. Perfect bisque head, appropriate wig, paperweight eyes, closed mouth, pierced ears; jointed composition body; appropriate clothes; all in good condition.

Mark:

B 9 F

18—20in (46—51cm) **$3200—3700**

See color photograph on page 74.

24in (61cm) *Paris Bébé. Wayne & Kay Jensen Collection.*

DEP
(Closed Mouth)

Maker: Unknown German porcelain factory
Date: 1885—1890
Material: Bisque head, jointed wood and composition French body
Mark: DEP

Marked DEP Child: Perfect bisque head, closed mouth, paperweight eyes, heavy eyebrows, painted upper and lower lashes, human hair wig; jointed French composition and wood body; dressed; all in good condition.

13—15in (33—38cm) **$1150—1350**
18—20in (46—51cm) **1800—2000**
24—26in (61—66cm) **2500—2750**

18in (46cm) *DEP* child. *Esther Schwartz Collection.*

D E P*
(Open Mouth)

Maker: Maison Jumeau, Paris, France; (heads possibly by Simon & Halbig, Gräfenhain, Thüringia, Germany)
Date: Late 1890s
Material: Bisque socket head, French jointed composition body (sometimes marked Jumeau)
Size: About 12—33in (31—84cm)
Mark: "DEP" and size number (up to 16 or so); sometimes stamped in red "Tete Jumeau;" body sometimes with Jumeau stamp or sticker

DEP: Perfect bisque socket head, human hair wig, sleep eyes, painted lower eyelashes only, upper hair eyelashes (sometimes gone), deeply molded eye sockets, open mouth, pierced ears; jointed French composition body; lovely clothes; all in good condition.

13—15in (33—38cm)	**$ 650—750**
18—20in (46—51cm)	**900—1000**
23—25in (58—64cm)	**1200—1300**
33—35in (84—89cm)	**2200—2400**

*The letters DEP appear in the mark of many dolls, but the particular dolls priced here have only "DEP" and a size number (unless they happen to have the red stamp "Tete Jumeau"). The face is characterized by deeply molded eye sockets and no painted upper eyelashes.

See color photograph on page 74.

17in (43cm) *DEP* child. *Private Collection.*

Doll House Dolls

Maker: Various German firms
Date: Ca. 1890—1920
Material: Bisque shoulder head, cloth body, bisque arms and legs
Size: Under 7in (18cm)
Mark: Sometimes "Germany"

Doll House Doll: Man or lady 5½—7in (14—18cm), as above with molded hair, painted eyes; original clothes or suitably dressed; all in nice condition.

Victorian lady,	**$150—165**
Victorian man with mustache	**175—225**
Lady with glass eyes and wig	**325—375**
Man with mustache, original Military uniform	**575—700**
Molded hair, glass eyes, ca. 1870, 6in (15cm)	**350—400**
Swivel neck, French-type head, 6½in (17cm)	**725**

6½in (17cm) early doll house lady with molded hair and glass eyes. *H&J Foulke, Inc.*

Door of Hope

Maker: Door of Hope Mission, China; heads by carvers from Ning-Po
Date: 1901 on
Material: Wooden heads; cloth bodies, sometimes with carved wooden hands
Size: Usually under 13in (33cm)
Mark: Sometimes "Made in China" label

Door of Hope: Carved wooden head with painted and/or carved hair, carved features; cloth body, sometimes carved hands; original handmade clothes, exact costuming for different classes of Chinese people; all in good condition. 25 dolls in the series.

Adult
  11—13in (28—33cm) **$250—350**
Child
  6—7in (15—18cm)   **375—425**
Mother and Baby
  11in (28cm)   **450—475**

Door of Hope Chinese bride in embroidered red outfit. *H&J Foulke, Inc.*

Grace G. Drayton

Maker: Various companies
Date: 1909—on
Material: All-cloth, or composition and cloth combination, or all-composition
Size: Various
Designer: Grace G. Drayton
Mark: Usually a cloth label or a stamp

G. G. Drayton

Puppy Pippin: 1911. Horsman Co., New York, N.Y., U.S.A. Composition head with puppy dog face, plush body with jointed legs; all in good condition. Cloth label. (For photograph see *7th Blue Book*, page 135.)
8in (20cm) sitting   **$375—400**

Campbell Kids, (see page 112).

"TRADE Puppy Pippin" Nov 24 11 MARK COPYRIGHT 1911 BY E.I. HORSMAN CO.

Peek-a-Boo: 1913—1915. Horsman Co., New York, N.Y., U.S.A. Composition head, arms, legs and lower torso, cloth upper torso; character face with molded hair, painted eyes to the side, watermelon mouth; dressed in striped bathing suit, polka dot dress or ribbons only; cloth label on outfit; all in good condition. (For photograph see *7th Blue Book*, page 136.)
7½in (19cm)   **$135—150**

11in (28cm) *Hug-Me Tight. Yvonne Baird Collection.*

Hug-Me-Tight: 1916. Colonial Toy Mfg. Co., New York, N.Y., U.S.A. Mother Goose characters and others in one piece, printed on cloth; all in good condition.
11in (28cm)   **$225—250**

Grace G. Drayton continued

Chocolate Drop: 1923. Averill Manufacturing Co., New York, N.Y., U.S.A. Brown cloth doll with movable arms and legs; painted features, three yarn pigtails; appropriate clothes; all in good condition. Stamped on front torso and paper label. (For photograph see *6th Blue Book*, page 120.)

11in (28cm)	**$325—375**
16in (41cm)	**500****

**Not enough price samples to compute a reliable range.

Dolly Dingle: 1923. Averill Manufacturing Co., New York, N.Y., U.S.A. Cloth doll with painted features and movable arms and legs; appropriate clothes; all in good condition. Stamped on front torso and paper label.

DOLLY DINGLE
COPYRIGHT BY
G.G. DRAYTON

11in (28cm)	**$300—350**
16in (41cm)	**450**

See color photograph on page 73.

14in (36cm) *G. G. Drayton child*, appropriate clothing. *H&J Foulke, Inc.*

Composition Child: Composition shoulder head, arms and legs, cloth torso; molded bobbed hair, watermelon mouth, painted eyes, round nose; original or appropriate clothes; in fair condition.

Mark:

14in (36cm)	**$350—400****

q · q · DRAYTON

**Not enough price samples to compute a reliable range.

Dressel

Maker: Cuno & Otto Dressel verlager & doll factory of Sonneberg, Thüringia, Germany. Heads by Armand Marseille, Simon & Halbig, Ernst Heubach, Gebrüder Heubach.

Date: 1700—on

Material: Composition wax over or bisque head, kid, cloth body or ball-jointed composition body

Trademarks: Fifth Ave. Dolls (1903), Jutta (1907), Bambina (1909), Poppy Dolls (1912), Holz-Masse (1875)

Mark:

13/0

Marked Holz-Masse Heads: 1875—on. Composition shoulder head, molded hair or sometimes mohair wig, usually painted eyes, sometimes pierced ears; cloth body with composition arms and legs with molded boots; old clothes; all in good condition.

MARK:

Molded hair:
16—18in (41—46cm)**$300—350**
22—24in (56—61cm) **375—425**
Wigged with glass eyes:
(Patent Washable)
16—18in (41—46cm) **325—375**
22—24in (56—61cm) **425—475**

15in (38cm) composition shoulder head of the type made by Dressel. *H&J Foulke, Inc.*

Dressel continued

Child Doll: 1893—on. Perfect bisque head, original jointed kid or composition body; good wig, glass eyes, open mouth; suitable clothes; all in good condition.

MARK: Various including those above and COD 93-3 DEP

Composition body:

16—18in (41—46cm) **$300—350***
22—24in (56—61cm) **400—450***
28—30in (71—76cm) **600—675***

Kid body:

14—16in (36—41cm) **250—275**
19—21in (48—53cm) **325—350**
24in (61cm) **400**

*Allow extra for fine bisque.

16in (41cm) child with fine bisque incised "COD" on composition body. *H&J Foulke, Inc.*

Portrait Series: 1896. ***Admiral Dewey*** and his men, ***Uncle Sam*** and perhaps others. Perfect bisque heads with portrait faces, glass eyes, some with molded mustaches and goatees; composition body; original clothes; all in good condition. Sometimes marked with "S" or "D" and a number. Heads by Simon & Halbig.

14—15in (36—38cm) **$1500—2000**

13in (33cm) ***Uncle Sam*** Portrait Doll incised "S 1." *Wenham Museum Collection, Wenham, Mass.*

Marked Jutta Child: Ca. 1906—1921. Perfect bisque socket head, good wig, sleep eyes, open mouth, pierced ears; ball-jointed composition body; dressed; all in good condition. Head made by Simon & Halbig. (For photograph see *7th Blue Book*, page 139.)

Mold *1348 or 1349*

MARK:

1349
Jutta
S & H
11

13—15in (33—38cm) **$375—425**
18—20in (46—51cm) **500—550**
22—24in (56—61cm) **600—700**
28—30in (71—76cm) **900—1000**

Dressel continued

Character Child: 1909—on. Perfect bisque socket head, ball-jointed composition body; mohair wig, painted eyes, closed mouth; suitable clothes; all in good condition. Glazed inside of head. (For photograph see *4th Blue Book*, page 83.)

16—17in (41—43cm)$2500—2600**

**Not enough price samples to compute a reliable range.

C.O.D. Character Baby: Ca. 1910—on. Perfect bisque character face with wig or molded hair, painted or glass eyes; jointed baby body; dressed; all in good condition.

13—15in (33—38cm)$325—375
18—20in (46—51cm) 425—500
22—24in (56—61cm) 600—700

Marked Jutta Character Baby: Ca. 1910—1922. Perfect bisque socket head, good wig, sleep eyes, open mouth; bent-limb composition baby body; dressed; all in good condition.

MARK:

Heubach 6½ Koppelsdorf
Jutta - Baby
Dressel
Germany
1922
10½

Jutta
1914
8

14—16in (36—41cm) $ 475—525
19—21in (48—53cm) 650—750
24in (61cm) 1000—1100

Toddler:
7—8in (18—20cm) 375—400
14—15in (36—38cm) 500—600
19—21in (48—53cm) 900—1100

Lady Doll: Ca. 1920s. Mold #1469. Bisque socket head with young lady face, good wig, sleep eyes, closed mouth; jointed composition body in adult form with molded bust, slim waist and long arms and legs, feet modeled to wear high-heeled shoes; appropriate clothes; all in good condition. (For photograph see *5th Blue Book*, page 117.)

MARK:

1469
C.O. Dressel
Germany
2

14in (36cm) $1500—1700

19in (48cm) Jutta 1914 toddler. *Anna May Case Collection.*

E. D. Bébé

Maker: Probably Danel & Cie or Etienne Denamur of Paris, France
Date: 1885—1895
Material: Bisque head, wood and composition jointed body
Mark:

E 8 D
DEPOSÉ

Marked E. D. Bébé: Perfect bisque head, wood and composition jointed body; good wig, beautiful blown glass eyes, pierced ears; nicely dressed; good condition. Often found on a marked Jumeau body.

Closed mouth:
 18—20in (46—51cm)$2500—2700
 24—26in (61—66cm) 3200—3600
 29—30in (74—75cm) 4000—4200
Open mouth:
 16—18in (41—46cm) 1400—1600
 22—24in (56—61cm) 2000—2300

See color photograph on page 75.

25in (64cm) *E.D. Esther Schwartz Collection.*

Eden Bébé

Maker: Fleischmann & Bloedel, doll factory, of Fürth, Bavaria, and Paris, France

Date: Founded in Bavaria in 1873. Also in Paris by 1890, then on into S.F.B.J. in 1899.

Material: Bisque head, composition jointed body

Trademark: Eden Bébé (1890), Bébé Triomphe (1898)

Mark: "EDEN BÉBÉ, PARIS"

Marked Eden Bebe: Ca. 1890. Perfect bisque head, fully-jointed or five-piece composition jointed body; beautiful wig, large set paperweight eyes, closed or open/closed mouth, pierced ears; lovely clothes; all in nice condition.

Closed mouth, 14—16in (36—41cm)   **$1900—2100**

20—22in (51—56cm)   **2500—2700**

Open mouth, 20—22in (51—56cm)   **1800—2000**

Kissing, Walking, Flirting Doll: 1892. Head from mold **1039** by Simon & Halbig, ball-jointed composition body with mechanism for walking, throwing kisses and flirting eyes. (For photograph see *7th Blue Book*, page 142.)

21—23in (53—58cm) **$875—975**

21in (53cm) *Eden Bébé* with open mouth.
Esther Schwartz Collection.

EFFanBEE

Maker: EFFanBEE Doll Co., New York, N.Y., U.S.A.
Date: 1912—on
Marks: Various, but nearly always marked "EFFanBEE" on torso or head.
Wore a metal heart-shaped bracelet; later a gold paper heart label.

EFFANBEE
DURABLE
DOLLS

Metal Heart Bracelet: **$45—50**

Baby Dainty: 1912—1922. Composition shoulder head, painted molded hair, painted facial features (sometimes with tin sleep eyes); cloth stuffed body jointed at shoulders and hips, with curved arms and straight legs of composition; original or appropriate old clothes; all in good condition. Came with metal heart bracelet.

MARK: First Mold: *Effanbee*
Second Mold: EFFANBEE
BABY DAINTY

15in (38cm) **$160—185**

Baby Grumpy: 1912—1939. Composition shoulder head with frowning face, molded and painted hair, painted eyes, closed mouth; composition arms and legs, cloth body; original or appropriate old clothes; all in good condition. Came with metal heart bracelet.

MARK:
EFFANBEE
DOLLS
WALK-TALK-SLEEP

12in (31cm), White **$165—185**
Black **235—265**

Early model, marked
172, 174 or *176:*
14—15in (36—38cm) **225—250**

12in (31cm) *Baby Grumpy*, brown complexion, all original. *Leone McMullen Collection.*

EFFanBEE continued

Mary Jane: 1917—1920. Composition "dolly face" head with metal sleeping eyes, painted eyebrows and eyelashes, open mouth with teeth, original human hair or mohair wig; jointed composition body with wood arms; dressed; all in very good condition. (For photograph see *7th Blue Book*, page 144.)

MARK: *Effanbee* back of head and torso in raised letters

$250—275

Bubbles: 1924—on. Composition head with blonde molded and painted hair, sleep eyes, open mouth with teeth, smiling face; cloth body, curved composition arms and legs; original or appropriate old clothes; all in good condition. Came with metal heart bracelet or necklace.

MARK: 19 © 24

EFFANBEE
DOLLS
WALK-TALK-SLEEP
MADE IN U.S.A.

EFFANBEE
BUBBLES
COPYR. 1924
MADE IN U.S.A.

16—18in (41—46cm)	**$225—250**
22—24in (56—61cm)	**300—350**
Black, 18in (46cm)	**550****

**Not enough price samples to compute a reliable range.

Marilee and Rosemary: 1924 (*Marilee*), 1925 (*Rosemary*). Composition shoulder head, human hair wig, open mouth, tin sleep eyes; cloth torso, composition arms and legs; original or appropriate old clothes; all in good condition. Came with metal heart bracelet.

MARK:

EFFANBEE
ROSEMARY
WALK-TALK-SLEEP

EFFANBEE
MARILEE
COPYR.
DOLL

14in (36cm)	**$175—190**
22in (56cm)	**225—250**

14in (36cm) *Rosemary*, all original. *H&J Foulke, Inc.*

EFFanBEE continued

Mae Starr: 1928. Composition shoulder head with human hair wig, sleep eyes, open/closed mouth; cloth body, composition limbs; talking device in center of torso with records.

MARK: MAE
STARR
DOLL

29—30in (74—76cm) **$425—475**

Mary Ann and Mary Lee: 1928-on. Composition head on *Lovums* shoulder plate, composition arms and legs, cloth torso; human hair wig, sleep eyes, open smiling mouth; appropriate clothes; in good condition. Later version came on an all-composition body marked "Patsy-Ann" for *Mary Ann* and "Patsy-Joan" for *Mary Lee*. Came with metal heart bracelet.

MARK: © MARY-ANN

16in (41cm) *Mary Lee*, all original. *H&J Foulke, Inc.*

16in (41cm) *Mary Lee* **$185—210**
19in (48cm) *Mary Ann* **225—250**

Lovums: 1928—1939. Composition swivel head on shoulder plate, arms and legs; molded painted hair or wig, pretty face, sleep eyes, smiling open mouth with teeth; cloth body; original or appropriate clothes; all in good condition. Came with metal heart bracelet. Note: The "Lovums" shoulder plate was used for many other dolls as well.

MARK: EFFANBEE
LOVUMS
©
PAT. Nº. 1,283,558

16—18in (41—46cm) **$210—235**
22—24in (56—61cm) **275—325**

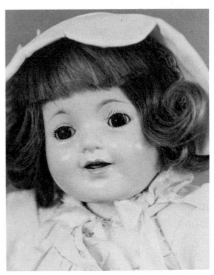

18in (46cm) *Lovums*, all original. *H&J Foulke, Inc.*

EFFanBEE continued

Patsy Family: 1928—on. All-composition, jointed at neck, shoulders and hips; molded hair (sometimes covered with wig), bent right arm on some members, painted or sleep eyes; original or appropriate old clothes; may have some crazing. Came with metal heart bracelet.

MARK:

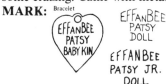

EFFanBEE
PATSY
DOLL

EFFANBEE
PATSY JR.
DOLL

6in (15cm) *Wee Patsy*, all original	**$300—325**	
7in (18cm) *Baby Tinyette*	175—185	
9in (23cm) *Patsy Babyette*	185—200	
Patsyette	200—225	
11in (28cm) *Patsy Baby*	210—235	
Patsy Jr.	250—275	
Patricia Kin	250—275	
14in (36cm) *Patsy*	275—325	
Patricia	275—325	
16in (41cm) *Patsy Joan*	300—350	
19in (48cm) *Patsy Ann*	300—350	
22in (56cm) *Patsy Lou*	375—425	
26in (66cm) *Patsy Ruth*	**500 up**	
30in (76cm) *Patsy Mae*	**500 up**	

14in (36cm) 1948 *Patsy*, all original. *H&J Foulke, Inc.*

14in (36cm) *Patsy* with sleep eyes and wig. *H&J Foulke, Inc.*

9in (23cm) *Patsy Babyette*, all original. *H&J Foulke, Inc.*

EFFanBEE continued

7in (18cm) *Baby Tinyette* with straight legs, all original. *H&J Foulke, Inc.*

19in (48cm) *Patsy Ann*, all original. *H&J Foulke, Inc.*

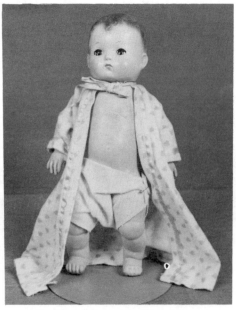

16in (41cm) *Patsy Joan*, all original. *H&J Foulke, Inc.*

11in (28cm) *Patsy Baby* with magic skin body. *H&J Foulke, Inc.*

EFFanBEE continued

Skippy: 1929. All-composition, jointed at neck, hips and shoulders, (later a cloth torso, still later a cloth torso and upper legs with composition molded boots for lower legs); molded hair, painted eyes to the side; original or appropriate clothes; all in good condition. Came with metal heart bracelet.

MARK: EFFANBEE
SKIPPY
©
P. L. Crosby

14in (36cm) $325—375

See color photograph on page 76.

Composition Girl with Molded Hair: Ca. 1930. All-composition, jointed at neck, shoulders and hips; molded hair painted brown, large painted eyes looking left, closed mouth; original clothes; all in good condition. (For photograph see *7th Blue Book*, page 148.)

MARK: EFFANBEE
MADE IN U.S.A.

9in (23cm) $150—165

Betty Brite: 1933. All-composition, jointed at neck, shoulders and hips; caracul wig, sleep eyes, open mouth with teeth; original or appropriate clothes; all in good condition. (For photograph see *6th Blue Book*, page 130.)

MARK: On torso: "EFFANBEE
BETTY BRITE"

16½in (42cm) $225—250

Lamkin: 1930s. Composition head, arms and legs with very deep and detailed molding, cloth body; molded hair, sleep eyes, bow mouth; original or appropriate clothes; all in good condition. (For photograph see *6th Blue Book*, page 129.)

MARK: On head:

"LAMBKINS"
(note spelling)

Paper heart tag: "Lamkin"

16in (41cm) $275—325

EFFanBEE continued

Dy-Dee Baby: 1933—on. First dolls had hard rubber head with soft rubber body, caracul wig or molded hair, open mouth for drinking, soft ears (after 1940). Later dolls had hard plastic heads with rubber bodies. Still later dolls had hard plastic heads with vinyl bodies. Came with paper heart label. Various sizes from 9—20in (23—51cm). Very good condition.

MARK:
"EFF-AN-BEE
DY-DEE BABY
US PAT.-1-857-485
ENGLAND-880-060
FRANCE-723-980
GERMANY-585-647
OTHER PAT PENDING"
Rubber body:

14—16in (36—41cm)	**$100—125**
24in (61cm)	**225—275**

Anne Shirley: 1935—1940. All-composition, jointed at neck, shoulders and hips; human hair wig, sleep eyes, closed mouth; original clothes; all in very good condition. Came with metal heart bracelet. "Anne Shirley" body used on other dolls as well.

MARK: On back:
"EFFanBEE/ANNE SHIRLEY."

14—15in (36—38cm)	**$200—225**
17—18in (43—46cm)	**250—275**
21in (53cm)	**300—325**
27in (69cm)	**450**

Sugar Baby: 1936. Composition head, curved arms and toddler legs, cloth body; molded hair or caracul wig, sleep eyes, closed mouth; appropriately dressed; all in very good condition. (For photograph see *5th Blue Book*, page 126.)

MARK:
"EFFanBEE
SUGAR BABY"

16—18in (41—46cm)	**$210—235**

14in (36cm) *Anne Shirley*, all original. *Esther Schwartz Collection.*

EFFanBEE continued

American Children: 1936-1939. Composition swivel head on composition *Anne Shirley* body, jointed at shoulders and hips. Four different faces designed by Dewees Cochran with either open or closed mouths, human hair wigs, painted or sleep eyes; original clothes; all in excellent condition. Came with metal heart bracelet and paper heart label. Sizes: 15in (38cm), 17in (43cm), 19in (48cm) and 21in (53cm).

MARK: On head: "EFFANBEE//AMERICAN//CHILDREN"
On body: "EFFANBEE//ANNE SHIRLEY"
The boy and the open-mouth girl are not marked.

Open mouth:
15in (38cm) *Barbara Joan* $ 550—600
17½in (45cm) *Barbara Ann*   650—700
21in (53cm) *Barbara Lou*   750—800
Closed mouth:
19—21in (48—53cm)   1100—1200
17in (43cm) boy   1100—1200

Charlie McCarthy: 1937. Composition head, hands and feet, cloth body; painted hair and eyes; strings at back of head to operate mouth; original clothes; all in very good condition.

MARK:
"EDGAR BERGEN'S CHARLIE McCARTHY,
AN EFFanBEE PRODUCT"
17—20in (43—51cm)   **$325—375**

15in (38cm) *Barbara Joan*, all original. *Esther Schwartz Collection.*

20in (51cm) *Charlie McCarthy*, all original. *Yvonne Baird Collection.*

EFFanBEE continued

Historical Dolls: 1939. All-composition, jointed at neck, shoulders and hips. Three each of 30 dolls portraying the history of American fashion, 1492—1939. "American Children" heads used with elaborate human hair wigs and painted eyes; elaborate original costumes using velvets, satins, silks, brocades, and so forth; all in excellent condition. Came with metal heart bracelet.

MARKS: On head: "EFFANBEE AMERICAN CHILDREN"
On body: "EFFANBEE ANNE SHIRLEY"
21in (53cm)   **$1250—1500**

See color photograph on page 75.

Historical Doll Replicas: 1939. All-composition, jointed at neck, shoulders and hips. Series of 30 dolls, popular copies of the original historical models (see above). Human hair wigs, painted eyes; original costumes all in cotton, copies of those on the original models. Came with metal heart bracelet. All in excellent condition.

MARK: On torso: "EFFanBEE
                    ANNE SHIRLEY"
14in (36cm)   **$400—450**

See color photograph on page 76.

Button Nose: Ca. 1939. All-composition with swivel head, joints at shoulders and hips; brown molded hair or mohair wig, painted eyes, closed mouth; appropriately dressed; all in very good condition.

MARK: "EFFANBEE"
9in (23cm)   **$175—200**

9in (23cm) *Button Nose* with wig. *H&J Foulke, Inc.*

EFFanBEE continued

Suzette: 1939. All-composition, jointed at neck, shoulders and hips; mohair wig, eyes painted to the side, closed mouth; original clothes; all in very good condition. Came with metal heart bracelet.

MARK: SUZETTE
EFF AN BEE
MADE IN
U.S.A.

11½in (29cm)   **$175—200**

Tommy Tucker: 1939—1949. Composition head with painted hair or mohair wig, flirting eyes, closed mouth, chubby cheeks; composition hands, stuffed body; original clothes; all in very good condition. Also called *Mickey* and *Baby Bright Eyes.* Came with paper heart tag. Sizes: 15—24in (38—61cm).

MARK: On head: "EFFANBEE
U.S.A."
16—18in (41—46cm)   **$210—235**
22—24in (56—61cm)   **275—325**

Suzanne: 1940. All-composition jointed at neck, shoulders and hips; mohair wig, sleep eyes, closed mouth; original clothes; all in very good condition. Came with metal heart bracelet.

MARK: SUZANNE
EFFANBEE
MADE IN U.S.A

14in (36cm)   **$225—250**

14in (36cm) *Suzanne* with magnetic hand, all original. *H&J Foulke, Inc.*

EFFanBEE continued

Little Lady: 1940—1949. All composition, jointed at neck, shoulders and hips, separated fingers; mohair or human hair wig, sleep eyes, closed mouth; same face as *Anne Shirley*; original clothes; all in very good condition. (During "war years" some had yarn wigs and/or painted eyes.) Various sizes.

MARK: On back: "EFFanBEE
     U.S.A.
   Paper heart: 'I am Little Lady' "

14—15in (36—38cm)	**$200**—225	
17—18in (43—46cm)	250—275	
20—21in (51—53cm)	300—325	
Brown complexion,		
20—21in (51—53cm)	**400**—450	

Portrait Dolls: 1940. All-composition, jointed at neck, shoulders and hips; mohair wigs, sleep eyes; in costumes, such as ballerina, *Bo-Peep, Gibson Girl*, bride and groom, dancing couple, all original, in excellent condition. (For photograph see *7th Blue Book*, page 152.)

MARK: None
11in (28cm)   **$200**—225

Brother and Sister: 1942. Composition swivel heads and hands, stuffed cloth body, arms and legs; yarn wig, painted eyes. Original pink (sister) and blue (brother) outfits. All in very good condition.

MARK: "EFFANBEE"
12in (31cm) *Sister*   **$160**—175
16in (41cm) *Brother*   180—195

14in (36cm) *Little Lady*, all original.
Esther Schwartz Collection.

EFFanBEE continued

Sweetie Pie: 1942. Composition head and limbs, cloth torso; caracul wig, flirty eyes, closed mouth; original clothes; all in very good condition. Available in 16in (41cm), 20in (51cm) and 24in (61cm).
MARK: "EFFANBEE © 1942"
16—18in (41—46cm)   **$210**—235
22—24in (56—61cm)   **275**—325
All composition,
16in (41cm)   **250**—265

Candy Kid: 1946. All-composition toddler, jointed at neck, shoulders and hips; molded hair, sleep eyes; original clothes; all in very good condition. Came with paper heart tag.
MARK: "EFFanBEE"
12in (31cm)   **$250**—275

Honey: 1949—1955. All-hard plastic, jointed at neck, shoulders and hips; synthetic, mohair or human hair, sleep eyes; original clothes; all in excellent condition.
MARK: EFFANBEE
14in (36cm)   **$150**—175
18in (46cm)   **200**—225
24in (61cm)   **275**—300

Effanbee Limited Edition Dolls: 1975—on. All-vinyl jointed doll; original clothes; excellent condition.
1975 **Precious Baby**   **$350**
1976 **Patsy**   350
1977 **Dewees Cochran**   200
1978 **Crowning Glory**   175
1979 **Skippy**   325
1980 **Susan B. Anthony**   175
1981 **Girl with Watering Can**   175
1982 **Princess Diana**   150
1983 **Sherlock Holmes**   150

16in (41cm) all-composition *Sweetie Pie,* all original. *H&J Foulke, inc.*

18in (46cm) **Honey.** *Doodlebug Doll & Toy Shop.*

Maud Tousey Fangel

Maker: Averill Manufacturing Co. and Georgene Novelties, New York, N.Y., U.S.A.

Date: 1938

Material: All-cloth

Size: 10in (25cm) and up

Designer: Maude Tousey Fangel

Mark: "M.T.F.©" at side of face on hair, but often inside the seam

---

Maud Tousey Fangel Doll: All-cloth with printed face in several variations which came dressed as a baby or child; some bodies are of printed cloth, some plain; soft stuffed, flexible arms and legs; original or appropriate clothes; all in good condition. *Snooks, Sweets* and possibly other names.

12in (31cm) $450—550

12in (31cm) *Sweets*, all original. *Private Collection.*

Farnell

Maker: J. K. Farnell Co., Ltd., Alpha Works Acton, London, England
Date: 1915—on
Material: Felt and cloth
Trademark: Alpha Toys
Mark: Cloth label on foot

See photo below

Child: 1925. All-cloth with felt face, painted features, mohair wig; cloth body
jointed at neck, shoulders and hips; original clothes; all in good condition.

Child, 14in (36cm)	**$325—350**
Coronation Doll of King George VI, 1937. 16in (41cm)	**350—400**
Baby, 10in (25cm)	**250—275****

**Not enough price samples to compute a reliable range.

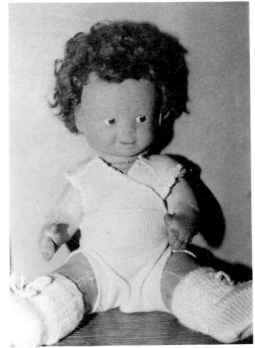

10in (25cm), label on foot, "Alpha
Toys" Baby. *Courtesy of Carolyn
Guzzio.*

French Bébé
(Unmarked)

Maker: Numerous French firms
Date: Ca. 1880—1925
Material: Bisque head, jointed composition body
Mark: None, except perhaps numbers, Paris, or France

Unmarked French Bébé: Perfect bisque head, swivel neck, lovely wig, set paperweight eyes, closed mouth, pierced ears; jointed French body; pretty costume; all in good condition.

Early, fine quality (desirable face):

14—16in (36—41cm)	**$3200—3600**
20—22in (51—56cm)	**4600—5000**

Standard quality:

17—19in (43—48cm)	**2000—2200**
22—24in (56—61cm)	**2600—2900**

Open Mouth:

1890s:

16—18in (41—46cm)	**1400—1600**
24—25in (61—64cm)	**2000—2200**

1920s:

17—19in (43—48cm)	**650—700**
23—24in (58—61cm)	**850—900**

20in (51cm) unmarked bébé of French quality on jointed French body. *Ruth Noden Collection.*

French Fashion-Type

Maker: Various French firms
Date: Ca. 1860—1930
Material: Bisque shoulder head, jointed kid body, some with bisque lower limbs or wood arms; or fully-jointed wood body sometimes covered with kid.
(See also *Bru, Jumeau, Gaultier, Gesland, Huret, Rohmer,* and *Barrois*)

French Fashion Lady: Perfect unmarked bisque shoulder head, swivel or stationary neck, kid body, kid arms -- some with wired fingers or old bisque arms; original or good wig, lovely blown glass eyes, closed mouth, earrings; appropriate clothes; all in good condition. Fine quality bisque.

12—13in (31—33cm)	**$1600 and up***
15—16in (38—41cm)	**2100 and up***
18—19in (46—48cm)	**2600 and up***
21in (53cm)	**3000 and up***
Fully-jointed wood body,	
16—19in (38—48cm)	**3500 and up+**
Radiguet & Cordonnier lady,	
17in (43cm) auction	**8200**

*Allow at least $400 additional for kid-over-wood upper and bisque lower arms.
*Greatly depending upon the appeal of the face.
*Allow extra for original clothing.
+ Allow extra for joints at ankle and waist.

See color photographs on pages 76 and 77.

18in (46cm) French fashion young lady with fully-jointed wood body. *Yvonne Baird Collection.*

Freundlich

Maker: Freundlich Novelty Corp., New York, N.Y., U.S.A.
Date: 1923—on
Material: All-composition

Baby Sandy: 1939—1942. All-composition with swivel head, jointed shoulders and hips, chubby toddler body; molded hair, smiling face, larger sizes have sleep eyes, smaller ones painted eyes; appropriate clothes; all in good condition.

MARK: On head: "Baby Sandy"
            On pin: "The Wonder Baby
                     Genuine Baby Sandy Doll"

8in (20cm)	**$110—125**
12in (31cm)	**150—175**
14—15in (36—38cm)	**225—275**

General Douglas MacArthur: Ca. 1942. All-composition portrait doll, molded hat, painted features, one arm to salute if desired; jointed shoulders and hips; original khaki uniform; all in good condition. (For photograph see *7th Blue Book*, page 161.)

MARK: Cardboard tag: "General MacArthur"
18in (46cm)   **$225—250**

Military Dolls: Ca. 1942. All-composition with molded hats, jointed shoulders and hips, character face, painted features; original clothes. ***Soldier, Sailor, WAAC,*** and ***WAVE,*** all in good condition. (For photograph see *7th Blue Book*, page 161.)

MARK: Cardboard tag
15in (38cm)   **$125—150**

12in (31cm) ***Baby Sandy***, all original. *H&J Foulke, Inc.*

Frozen Charlotte
(Bathing Doll)

Maker: Various German firms
Date: Ca. 1850s—early 1900s
Material: Glazed china; sometimes bisque
Size: 1—18in (3—46cm)
Mark: None, except for "Germany," or numbers or both

Frozen Charlotte: All-china doll, black or blonde molded hair parted down
the middle, painted features; hands extended, legs separated but not jointed;
no clothes; perfect condition. Good quality.

2—3in (5—8cm)	$ 35—45*
4—5in (10—13cm)	80—95*
6—7in (15—18cm)	125—150*
10—11in (25—28cm)	225—250*
14—15in (36—38cm)	325—375*
Pink tint, early hairdo 5in (13cm)	165—185
Pink tint with bonnet, 5in (13cm)	300—325
Tinted bisque, blonde hair, 5in (13cm)	135—160
Parian-type (untinted bisque), 5in (13cm)	150—175
Alice style with pink boots (bisque), 5in (13cm)	250—275
China with long molded blonde braids and bows, 4½in (12cm)	275—300

*Allow extra for pink tint, fine decoration and modeling and unusual hairdos.

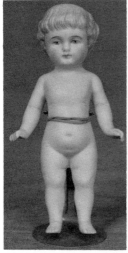

5in (13cm) bisque Frozen
Charlotte. *Private Collection.*

4½in (12cm) Frozen
Charlotte with molded
shift trimmed with
painted flowers.
*Yvonne Baird
Collection.*

6½in (17cm) Frozen Charlotte.
Yvonne Baird Collection.

Fulper

Maker: Heads by Fulper Pottery Co. of Flemington, N.J., U.S.A.
for other companies, often Amberg or Horsman
Date: 1918—1921
Material: Bisque heads; composition ball-jointed or jointed kid bodies
Mark: "Fulper—Made in U.S.A."

Made in
USA
13

Fulper Child Doll: Perfect bisque head, good wig; kid jointed or composition ball-jointed body; set or sleep eyes, open mouth; suitably dressed; all in good condition. Good quality bisque.

Kid body, 16—19in (41—48cm)   **$350—400***
Composition body, 18—20in (46—51cm) **475—525***

Fulper Baby or Toddler: Same as above, but with bent-limb or jointed toddler body.

14—16in (36—41cm)   **$450—550***
20—22in (51—56cm)   **650—750***

Character Child: Molded hair, intaglio eyes, open/closed mouth.
17in (43cm) at auction   **$2000**

*Do not pay as much for a doll with poor bisque.

20in (51cm) Fulper child. *H&J Foulke, Inc.*

Gaultier

Maker: Francois Gauthier (name changed to Gaultier in 1875); St. Maurice, Charenton, Seine, Paris, France (This company made only porcelain parts, not bodies.)

Date: 1860 to 1899 (then joined S.F.B.J.)

Material: Bisque head for kid or composition body; all-bisque

---

Marked F. G. Fashion Lady:
1860 to 1930. Bisque swivel head on bisque shoulder plate, original kid body, kid arms with wired fingers or bisque lower arms and hands; original or good French wig, lovely large stationary eyes, closed mouth, ears pierced; dressed; all in good condition.

MARK:
"F.G." on side of shoulder

12—13in (31—33cm)	**$1100—1300***
17—18in (43—46cm)	**1800—2000***
22—23in (56—58cm)	**2400—2600***
26—27in (66—69cm)	**2900—3100***

Wood body,
17—18in (43—46cm) **2800—3000***

Late doll in ethnic costume:
8—9in (20—23cm)	**500—600**
12in (31cm)	**800—850**

*Allow extra for original costume.

See color photograph on page 77.

8½in (22cm) late F. G. lady with painted eyes and hair, all original provincial costume. *Joanna Ott Collection.*

Gaultier continued

Marked F. G. Bébé: Ca. 1879—
1887. Bisque swivel head on
shoulder plate and gusseted kid
body with bisque lower arms or
chunky jointed composition
body; good wig, large bulgy
paperweight eyes, closed mouth,
pierced ears; dressed; all in good
condition.

MARK: "F. 7 G."
(or other size number) So-called
"Block letters" mark.

14—16in (38—41cm) **$2600—2800**
18—20in (46—51cm) **3000—3300**
23—25in (58—64cm) **3800—4200**

See color photograph on page 78.

21in (53cm) F.G. (block letters) child.
Yvonne Baird Collection.

Marked F. G. Bébé: Ca. 1887—
1900 and probably later. Bisque
head, composition jointed body;
good French wig, beautiful large
set eyes, closed mouth, pierced
ears; well dressed; all in good
condition.

MARK: So-called "Scroll"
mark.

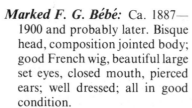

5—6in (13—15cm)   **$ 500—600**
15—17in (38—43cm) **1900—2300**
21—23in (53—58cm) **2600—2800**
28—29in (71—74cm) **3300—3600**
Open mouth:
  15—17in (38—43cm) **1300—1600**
  20—22in (51—56cm) **1700—2000**
  28—29in (71—74cm) **2500—2600**

5in (13cm) F.G. child incised also "C" on
front neck. *H&J Foulke, Inc.*

German Bisque
(Unmarked or Unidentified Marks)

Maker: Various German firms
Date: 1860s—on
Material: Bisque head, composition, kid or cloth body
Mark: Some numbered, some "Germany," some both

Molded Hair Doll: Ca. 1880.
Tinted bisque shoulder head with
beautifully molded hair (usually
blonde), painted eyes (sometimes
glass), closed mouth; original kid
or cloth body; bisque lower arms;
appropriate clothes; all in good
condition.

5—7in (13—18cm)	**$ 100—125**
12—14in (31—36cm)	**200—250***
15—18in (38—46cm)	**275—350***
20—23in (51—58cm)	**400—450***
Unusual hairdo,	
16in (41cm)	**500 up**
Glass eyes,	
18—20in (46—51cm)	
Common hairdo,	**550—650**

Heavily decorated shoulder plate,
elaborate hair, painted eyes,
21in (53cm) **1600**

*Allow extra for unusual hairdo
and glass eyes.

So-called *American School Boy:*
Glass eyes. (For photograph
see *7th Blue Book*, page 168.)
14—15in (36—38cm) **400—450**

ABOVE RIGHT: 16in (41cm) molded
hair child. *Joe Jackson and Joel Pearson.*

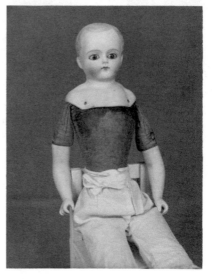

13in (33cm) molded hair boy with glass
eyes. *Private Collection.*

German Bisque continued

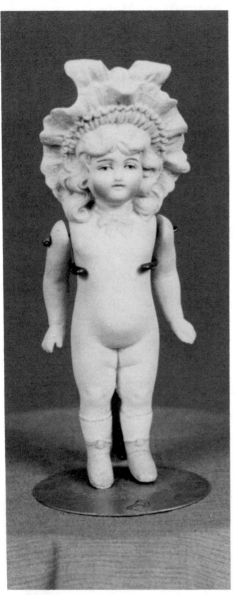

Hatted or Bonnet Doll: Ca. 1880—1920. Bisque head with painted molded hair and molded fancy bonnet with bows, ribbons, flowers, feathers, and so forth; painted eyes and facial features; original cloth body with bisque arms and legs; good old clothes or nicely dressed; all in good condition.

12—15in (31—38cm)
  "Marqueritas" stone bisque
  (Hertwig & Co.)   **$ 200—250***
15—16in (38—41cm)
  fine quality (A.B.G.)   **400—500***
18in (46cm) black hair,
  molded gray hat,
  glass eyes   **1800****
24in (61cm) blonde hair,
  orange bonnet,
  glass eyes
  (A.B.G. *#1024*)   **2800****
All-bisque,
  6—7in (15—18cm)   **150—200***

*Allow extra for unusual style.

**Not enough price samples to compute a reliable range.

7in (18cm) all-bisque with molded hat tinted pink and blue. *H&J Foulke, Inc.*

German Bisque continued

Child Doll with closed mouth: Ca. 1880—1890. Perfect bisque head; kid or
cloth body, gusseted at hips and knees with good bisque hands or jointed
composition body; good wig; nicely dressed; all in good condition.

Kid or cloth body,

12—13in (31—33cm)	$ 500—600*
15—17in (38—43cm)	550—600*
20—22in (51—56cm)	700—800*
26in (66cm)	1000*

*Allow extra for a swivel neck or
unusual face.

Composition body:

13—15in (33—38cm)	1000—1200
19—21in (48—53cm)	1600—1800
24—25in (61—64cm)	2000—2300

14in (36cm) closed mouth child, all
original. *H&J Foulke, Inc.*

Child Doll with open mouth "Dolly Face:" 1888 on. Perfect bisque head,
ball-jointed composition body or kid body with bisque lower arms; good wig,
glass eyes, open mouth; dressed; all in good condition.

Very good quality:

12in (31cm)	$300
14—16in (36—41cm)	350—375
18—20in (46—51cm)	450—500
23—24in (48—51cm)	550—600
28—30in (71—76cm)	850—950

Standard quality:

12—14in (31—36cm)	$250—275
16—18in (41—46cm)	325—375
22—24in (56—61cm)	425—475
28—30in (71—76cm)	650—750

See color photograph on page 78.

25in (64cm) unmarked child with open
mouth. *H&J Foulke, Inc.*

German Bisque continued

22in (56cm) child with open mouth incised "1902." *H&J Foulke, Inc.*

15in (38cm) child incised "G-2." *H&J Foulke, Inc.*

Tiny child doll: 1890 to World War I. Perfect bisque socket head of good quality, five-piece composition body of good quality with molded and painted shoes and stockings; good wig, set or sleep eyes, open mouth; cute clothes; all in good condition.

5—6in (13—15cm)	**$175—200**
8—10in (20—25cm)	**225—275**
Fully-jointed body,	
7—8in (18—20cm)	**275—325**
Closed mouth:	
4½—5½in (12—14cm)	**225—250**
8in (20cm)	**350—400**

4in (10cm) tiny child doll, all original. *H&J Foulke, Inc.*

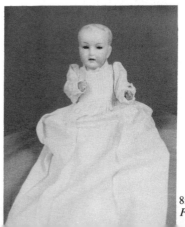
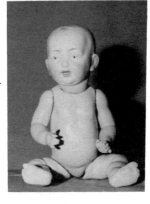

German Bisque continued

Character Baby: 1910—on. Perfect bisque head, good wig or solid dome with painted hair, sleep eyes, open mouth; composition bent-limb baby body; suitably dressed; all in good condition.

8—9in (20—23cm)	$225—275*
12—14in (31—36cm)	400—450*
17—19in (43—48cm)	525—575*
22—24in (56—61cm)	700—800*
Painted eyes:	
7—8in (18—20cm)	$225—250*
12in (31cm)	400—425

*Allow more for open/closed mouth, closed mouth or unusual face.

9½in (24cm) 199 character baby. *H&J Foulke, Inc.*

17in (43cm) character baby with painted upper teeth. *H&J Foulke, Inc.*

12in (31cm) character baby with painted eyes. *Private Collection.*

8in (20cm) B-5/0 character baby. *H&J Foulke, Inc.*

German Bisque continued

Character Child: 1910—on. Bisque head with good wig or solid dome head with painted hair, sleep or painted eyes, open or closed mouth, expressive character face; jointed composition body; dressed; all in good condition.

17—18in (43—46cm)   **$1800 up***

#111, 128
   18—20in (45—51cm)   **8000 up****

*Depending upon individual face.
**Not enough price samples to compute a reliable range.

Infant, unmarked or unidentified maker: 1924—on. Perfect bisque head with molded and painted hair, glass sleep eyes; cloth body, celluloid or composition hands; dressed; all in good condition.

10—12in (25—31cm) long   **$325—375***
15—18in (38—46cm) long   **525—625***

*More depending upon appeal and rarity of face.

19in (48cm) character child incised "128." *Ralph's Antique Dolls.*

Gesland

Maker: Heads: François Gaultier, Paris, France
Bodies: E., F. & A. Gesland, Paris, France
Date: Late 1860s—on
Material: Bisque head, stockinette stuffed body on wire frame, bisque or composition lower arms and legs
Mark: Head: **F. G** Body: Sometimes stamped E. Gesland

Fashion lady: Perfect bisque swivel head, good wig, paperweight eyes, closed mouth, pierced ears; stockinette body with bisque hands and legs; dressed; all in good condition.
16—20in (41—51cm) **$3200—3700***

*For beautiful early face.

Bébé: Perfect bisque swivel head; composition shoulder plate, good wig, paperweight eyes, closed mouth, pierced ears; stockinette body with composition lower arms and legs; dressed; all in good condition.
16—18in (41—46cm) **$3200—3500***
21—24in (53—61cm) **4200—4500***
25in (64cm) spectacular
   face at auction   **8800***
33in (84cm) at auction **6250***
*For beautiful early face.

18in (46cm) Gesland bébé with F. G. (block letters) head. *Elizabeth McIntyre.*

Giebeler-Falk

Maker: Giebeler-Falk Doll Corporation, New York, N.Y., U.S.A.
Date: 1918—1921
Material: Aluminum head, sometimes aluminum hands and feet, wood or composition torso, arms and legs
Size: 16, 18, 20, 22 and 25in (41, 46, 51, 56 and 64cm)
Mark:

U. S. PAT.

Marked Giebeler-Falk Doll: Aluminum head with smiling face, open/closed mouth with painted upper teeth, metal sleeping eyes, chin dimple, mohair wig; jointed wood or composition body, sometimes with metal hands and feet with jointed ankles; appropriate clothing; all in good condition.
16—18in (46—51cm) **$250—275**
22—25in (56—64cm) **300—325**

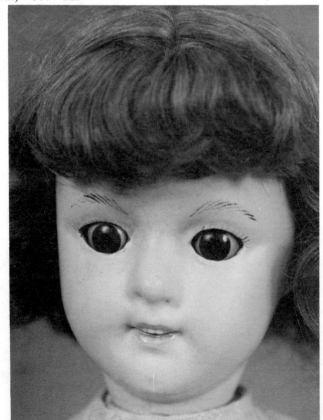

25in (64cm) unmarked doll, probably by Giebeler-Falk. *H&J Foulke, Inc.*

15½in (39cm) J.D. Kestner 243 Oriental character baby. For further information see page 322. *Betty Lunz Collection.*

186

18in (46cm) *Munich Art Doll*. For further information see page 318. *Yvonne Baird Collection.*

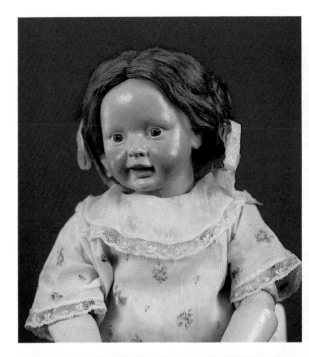

22in (56cm) Kley & Hahn 520 character child. For further information see page 281. *Joanna Ott Collection.*

16in (41cm) cloth Käthe Kruse children, Doll I models, all original. For further information see page 289. *Private Collection.*

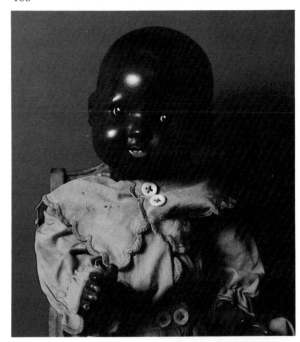

22in (56cm) Armand Marseille 351 black character baby. For further information see page 95. *H&J Foulke, Inc.*

19in (48cm) Armand Marseille 230 **Fany** character child. For further information see page 304. *Richard Wright Antiques.*

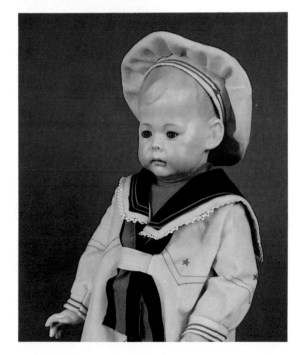

24in (61cm) Armand Marseille 990 character child. For further information see page 304. *H&J Foulke, Inc.*

18in (46cm) Armand Marseille 590 character child. For further information see page 304. *Yvonne Baird Collection.*

RIGHT: 25in (64cm) Armand Marseille *Queen Louise.* For further information see page 302. *H&J Foulke, Inc.*

ABOVE: 20in (51cm) *Bébé Mascotte*. For further information see page 309. *Joanna Ott Collection.*

LEFT: 13in (33cm) Armand Marseille 353 Oriental character baby. For further information see page 322. *Betty Lunz Collection.*

28in (71cm) papier-mâché
Greiner, 1858 label. For
further information see page
209. *Joanna Ott Collection.*

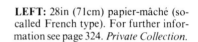

LEFT: 28in (71cm) papier-mâché (so-
called French type). For further information see page 324. *Private Collection.*

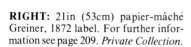

RIGHT: 21in (53cm) papier-mâché
Greiner, 1872 label. For further information see page 209. *Private Collection.*

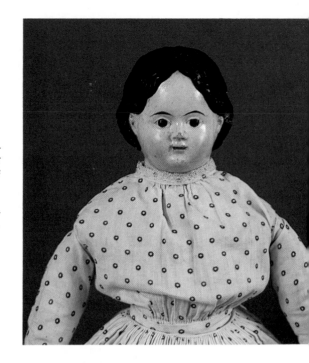

192

RIGHT: 20in (51cm) papier-mâché with painted eyes. For further information see page 337. *Private Collection.*

BELOW: 32in (81cm) papier-mâché by Lerch & Klag. *Private Collection.*

ABOVE LEFT: 24in (61cm) papier-mâché with label "No. 1879.//Industructible H[ead]//This composition//Perfectly harmle[ss]." For further information see page 326. *Yvonne Baird Collection.*

ABOVE RIGHT: 13in (33cm) brown bisque *Paris Bébé*. For further information see page 144. *Private Collection.*

RIGHT: Traditional Japanese papier-mâché portrait doll of a boy about 3 years of age, Ca. 1900, all original. For further information see page 321. *Betty Lunz Collection.*

24in (61cm) Parian lady with molded necklace, earrings and hair band. For further information see page 328. *Yvonne Baird Collection.*

LEFT: 18in (46cm) *Philadelphia Baby*, all original. For further information see page 332. *H&J Foulke, Inc.*

BELOW: 16in (41cm) Molly-'es *Raggedy Ann & Andy*, all original. For further information see page 340. *H&J Foulke, Inc.*

13in (33cm) S.F.B.J. 251 character toddler. For further information see page 348. *Private Collection.*

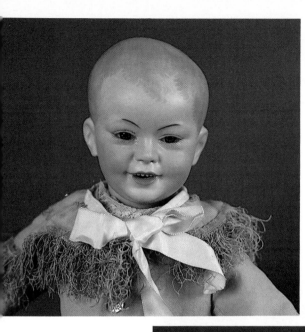

17in (43cm) S.F.B.J. 227 character child. For further information see page 348. *Private Collection.*

12in (31cm) S.F.B.J. brown bisque child. For further information see page 347. *Private Collection.*

19in (48cm) all-wood Schoenhut model #314. For further information see page 356. *Private Collection.*

24in (61cm) Porzellanfabrik Burggrub 169 character baby. For further information see page 354. *H&J Foulke, Inc.*

17in (43cm) all-wood Schoenhut model #102. For further information see page 356. *Private Collection.*

LEFT: 13in (33cm) all-composition Schoenhut child with label, all original. For further information see page 359. *H&J Foulke, Inc.*

BELOW: 16in (41cm) all-wood Schoenhut pouty girl model #310. For further information see page 356. *Esther Schwartz Collection.*

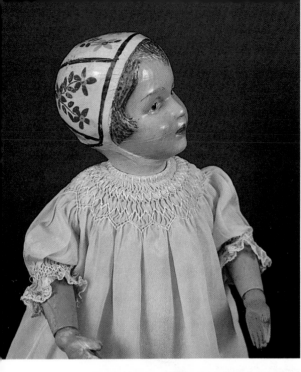

LEFT: 17in (43cm) all-wood Schoenhut girl with molded cap model #106. For further information see page 356. *Private Collection.*

BELOW: 11in (28cm) all-wood Schoenhut walking doll model #107W. For further information see page 358. *Private Collection.*

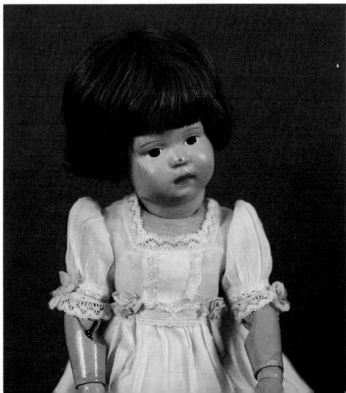

Gladdie

Maker: Heads made in Germany for George Borgfeldt, New York, N.Y., U.S.A.
Date: 1929
Material: Ceramic or bisque head, cloth torso, composition arms and legs
Size: 16—23in (41—58cm)
Designer: Helen W. Jensen
Mark:

[sic] *Gladdie*
Copyriht By
Helen W. Jensen

Marked Gladdie: Ceramic head, molded and painted hair, glass eyes, open/closed mouth with molded teeth, laughing face; cloth torso, composition arms and legs; dressed; all in good condition.
16—19in (41—48cm)   **$ 850—950**
Bisque head, 13in (33cm)   **3200****

**Not enough price samples to compute a reliable range.

13in (33cm) bisque head *Gladdie. Esther Schwartz Collection.*

Godey's Little Lady Dolls

Maker: Ruth Gibbs, Flemington, N.J., U.S.A.
Date: 1946
Material: China head and limbs, cloth body
Size: Most 7in (18cm); a few 9, 10, 12 or 13in (23, 25, 31 or 33cm)
Designer: Herbert Johnson
Mark: Paper label inside skirt "Godey's Little Lady Dolls;" "R. G." incised on back plate.

Ruth Gibbs Doll: China head with painted black, brown, blonde or auburn hair and features; pink cloth body with china limbs and painted slippers which often matched the hair color; original clothes, usually in an old-fashioned style.

7in (18cm)	**$ 60—65**
12 or 13in (31 or 33cm) undressed	**135—150**

13in (33cm) *Mrs. March,* all original. *H&J Foulke, Inc.*

Goebel

Maker: F. & W. Goebel porcelain factory, near Coburg, Thüringia, Germany
Date: 1879—on
Material: Bisque heads, composition bodies; also all-bisque
Mark: or "B" + number; "Germany"
sometimes A, C, G, H, K, S, SA & T

Goebel Child Doll: 1895—on. Perfect bisque socket head, good wig, sleep eyes, open mouth; composition jointed body; dressed; all in good condition. (For photograph see *6th Blue Book*, page 164.)

4½—5in (12—13cm)	**$150—165**
15—17in (38—43cm)	**275—325**
21—24in (53—61cm)	**350—450**

Socket head, open/closed mouth with molded teeth, gusseted kid body, bisque hands,
18—20in (46—51cm)   **600—700**

Pincushion Half Doll: Ca. 1915. Perfect china half figure usually of a lady with molded hair and painted features, sometimes with molded clothing, hats or accessories; lovely modeling and painting. Most desirable have fancy clothing or hair ornamentation and extended arms.

MARK:
2½in (6cm)   **$ 85—95**
4in (10cm)   **150 and up***

*Depending upon rarity.

19½in (50cm) Goebel child with open/closed mouth. *Esther Schwartz Collection.*

2½in (6cm) marked Goebel pincushion dolls. *H&J Foulke, Inc.*

Goebel continued

Goebel Character Baby: Ca. 1910. Perfect bisque socket head, good wig, sleep eyes, open mouth with teeth; composition jointed baby body; dressed; all in good condition.

18—21in (46—53cm)   **$450—550**
Toddler with smiling face **#B1-2,** 14in (36cm)   **675**

Goebel Character Doll: Ca. 1910. Perfect bisque head with molded hair in various styles, some with hats, character face smiling or somber with painted features; papier-mâché five-piece body; all in excellent condition.

6½in (17cm)   **$275—325**

6in (15cm) character girl with molded flowers in hair, all original. *H&J Foulke, Inc.*

Googly-Eyed Dolls

Maker: J. D. Kestner, Armand Marseille, Hertel, Schwab & Co., Heubach, H. Steiner, Goebel and other German and French firms

Date: Ca. 1911—on

Material: Bisque heads and composition or papier-mâché bodies or all-bisque

---

All-Bisque Googly: Jointed at shoulders and hips, molded shoes and socks; mohair wig, glass eyes, impish mouth; undressed; in perfect condition.

5in (13cm)	$ 450—500
Swivel neck, 5in (13cm)	600—650
7in (18cm)	850
Jointed elbows and knees (Kestner), 5in (13cm)	1800
7in (18cm)	2900
Painted eyes, 4—4½in (10—12cm)	300—350
Baby, 4½in (12cm)	400—425
K&R 131, 7in (18cm)	2000—2200

5in (13cm) 292 googlies with swivel necks, all original. *H&J Foulke, Inc.*

Painted eyes, composition body:
Perfect bisque swivel head with molded hair, painted eyes to the side, impish mouth; composition body jointed at shoulders and hips with molded and painted shoes and socks; cute clothes; all in good condition.

A.M., E. Heubach, Goebel, R.A.

6—7in (15—18cm)	$325—350
10in (25cm)	550—600
Gebrüder Heubach	
6—7in (15—18cm)	400—450

See color photograph on page 113.

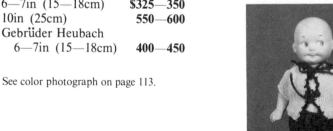

7in (18cm) A.M. 320 googly. *H&J Foulke, Inc.*

Googly-Eyed Dolls continued

Glass eyes, composition body: Perfect bisque head, mohair wig or molded hair, sleep or set large googly eyes, impish mouth closed; original composition body jointed at neck, shoulders and hips, sometimes with molded and painted shoes and socks; cute clothes; all in nice condition.

JDK 221:

12—13in (31—33cm) Toddler	$3500—4500
17—18in (43—46cm) Toddler	5500—6500

AM #323 and other similar models by H. Steiner, E. Heubach, Goebel and Recknagle:

6½—7in (17—18cm)	500—600
9—10in (23—25cm)	800—900
12—14in (31—36cm)	1400—1500
Baby body, 10—11in (25—28cm)	700—800

AM #253: Watermelon mouth:

6½—7½in (17—19cm)	600—700
9in (23cm)	900

SFBJ #245:

8in (20cm), 5 piece body	1200—1400
9in (23cm) JCB	2000
15in (38cm)	4500—5000**

K ★ R 131:

8in (20cm), 5 piece body	2600—2800
15—16in (38—41cm)	6500—7500**

AM #240, 241, 200:

11—12in (28—31cm)	2200—2700

Heubach Einco:

14—15in (36—38cm)	6000—7000**

Oscar Hitt:

15in (38cm)	6500—7500**

Hertel, Schwab & Co. #165:

11in (28cm) Baby	2500—2800
15in (38cm) Toddler	3500—4000

Hertel, Schwab & Co. #172, 173:

15—16in (38—41cm)	4500—5500**

Demalcol (Dennis, Malley, & Co. London, England)

9—11in (23—28cm)	550—650

Gebrüder Heubach #9573:

10in (25cm)	1300

Gebrüder Heubach Beth:

7½in (19cm)	750

B.P. 686:

12in (31cm) toddler	2500**

P.M. 950:

10½in (27cm) toddler	2000**

**Not enough price samples to compute a reliable range.

Googly-Eyed Dolls continued

13in (33cm) Hertel, Schwab & Co. 165 googly baby. *Esther Schwartz Collection.*

10½in (27cm) P.M. 950 googly on toddler body. *Richard Wright Antiques.*

7in (18cm) A.M. 323 googly, all original. *H&J Foulke, Inc.*

Googly-Eyed Dolls continued

Composition face: 1911—1914. Made by various companies in 9½—14in (24—36cm) sizes; marked with paper label on clothing. Called "Hug Me Kiddies," "Little Bright Eyes," as well as other trade names. Round all-composition or composition mask face, wig, round glass eyes looking to the side, watermelon mouth; felt body; original clothes; all in very good condition.

9—10in (23—25cm) **$500—600**
12in (31cm) **700—800**

12in (31cm) composition face googly, all original. *Private Collection.*

Googly with molded hat: 1915. Perfect bisque head with glass side-glancing eyes, watermelon mouth, molded hat; jointed composition body. Made for Max Handwerck, possibly by Hertel, Schwab & Co. All were soldiers: "U.S." (Uncle Sam hat); "E," (English Bellhop-type hat); "D," (German); "T," (Austrian/ Turk - two faces).
MARK:
"Dep
Elite"
12—13in (31—33cm) **$2000—2500**

10in (25cm) googly with German hat, open mouth. *Esther Schwartz Collection.*

Greiner

Maker: Ludwig Greiner of Philadelphia, PA., U.S.A.
Date: 1858—1883
Material: Heads of papier-mâché, cloth bodies, homemade in most cases, but later some Lacmann bodies were used.
Size: Various, 13—over 35in (33—over 89cm)
Mark: Paper label on back shoulder:

GREINER'S
IMPROVED
PATENTHEADS
Pat. March 30TH'58

or

GREINER'S
PATENT DOLL HEADS
No7
Pat. Mar. 30'58. Ext. '72

Greiner: Blonde or black molded hair, painted features; homemade cloth body, leather arms; nice old clothes; entire doll in good condition.

'58 label:

20—23in (51—58cm) $ 900—1200
28—30in (71—76cm) 1500—1700

Much worn:

20—23in (51—58cm) 500—600
28—30in (71—76cm) 700—800

Glass eyes,

20—23in (51—58cm) 1700—1900

'72 label:

19—22in (48—56cm) 450—500
29—31in (71—79cm) 700—800

See color photographs on page 191.

21in (53cm) '58 label Greiner. *Esther Schwartz Collection.*

H.G.

Maker: Unknown manufacturer, Paris, France
Date: Ca. 1880s
Material: Bisque head, jointed composition and wood body
Mark: PARIS
H.G.
II

H.G. Bébé: Perfect bisque head, appropriate wig, paperweight eyes, closed mouth; jointed composition and wood body; lovely clothing; all in good condition.
25—26in (64—66cm) **$12,500**

25½in (65cm) H.G. Bébé. *Jackie Kaner.*

Hamburger & Co.

Maker: Hamburger & Co., New York, N.Y., U.S.A. doll importer and producer contracted with various German doll factories.
Date: 1889—1909
Material: Bisque head, jointed composition body

Hamburger Viola: 1903. Perfect bisque socket head, original or appropriate wig, sleep or set eyes, open mouth; ball-jointed composition body; dressed; entire doll in good condition.

MARK: *Made in*
Germany
Viola
H. 6 Co.

23—25in (58—64cm)   **$400—450**

Other Hamburger Trademarks:
Santa 1900. Made by Simon & Halbig. See page 366.
Dolly Dimple 1907. Made by Gebrüder Heubach. See page 222.

25in (64cm) *Viola. H&J Foulke, Inc.*

Heinrich Handwerck

Maker: Heinrich Handwerck, doll factory, Waltershausen, Thüringia,
Germany. Heads by Simon & Halbig.

Date: 1855—on

Material: Bisque head, composition ball-jointed body or kid body

Trademarks: Bébé Cosmopolite, Bébé de Réclame, Bébé Superior

Mark: "Germany—Handwerck" sometimes with "S & H" and numbers 69, 79,
89, 99, 109, 119 and others

Hch 6/0 H.

HANDWERCK— Germany

Marked Handwerck Child Doll: Ca. 1885—on. Perfect bisque socket head,
original or good wig, sleep or set eyes, open mouth, pierced ears; ball-jointed
body; dressed; entire doll in good condition.

#79, 89 closed mouth:

12in (31cm)	**$1000**
18—20in (46—51cm)	**1500—1600**
24in (61cm)	**2000**

Open mouth:

14—16in (36—41cm)	**350—375**
19—21in (43—53cm)	**425—450**
23—25in (58—64cm)	**500—600**
28—30in (71—76cm)	**800—900**
33—35in (84—89cm)	**1200—1500**
42in (107cm)	**2700—2900**

Shoulder head, kid body

19—21in (48—53cm)	**325—375**

See color photograph on page 79.

18in (46cm) Hch H. shoulder head child,
all original. *H&J Foulke, Inc.*

Max Handwerck

Maker: Max Handwerck, doll factory, Waltershausen, Thüringia, Germany. Some heads by Goebel.

Date: 1900—on

Material: Bisque head, ball-jointed composition or kid body

Trademarks: Bébé Elite, Triumph-Bébé

Mark: also "Bébé Elite"

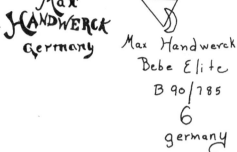

Marked Max Handwerck Child Doll: Perfect bisque socket head, original or good wig, set or sleep eyes, open mouth, pierced ears; original ball-jointed body; well dressed; all in good condition.

16—18in (41—46cm)	$350—400
19—21in (48—53cm)	425—450
25—26in (64—66cm)	600—700
30—31in (76—79cm)	900—950

Marked Bébé Elite Character: Perfect bisque socket head with sleep eyes, open mouth with upper teeth, smiling character face; bent-limb composition baby body; appropriate clothes; all in good condition. (For photograph see *6th Blue Book*, page 171.)

16—19in (41—48cm)	$425—525
23—25in (58—64cm)	650—750

31in (79cm) 283/33 Max Handwerck child. *Doodlebug Doll & Toy Shop.*

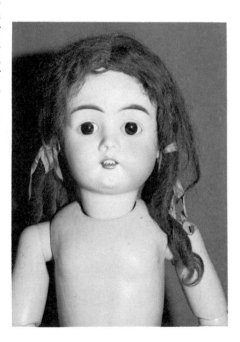

Carl Hartmann

Maker: Carl Hartmann, Neustad, Thüringia; Stockheim, Bavaria, Germany
Date: 1899 trademark
Material: Bisque head, composition body
Size: Various
Mark: Globe Baby
      DEP
      Germany
      C : H

Marked Globe Baby: Perfect bisque head, mohair or human hair wig, sleep
    eyes, open mouth with upper teeth; good quality five-piece composition body
    with molded shoes and socks; dressed; all in very good condition.
8in (20cm)   **$250—275**

8in (20cm) ***Globe Baby***, all original. *H&J Foulke, Inc.*

Hertel, Schwab & Co.

Maker: Stutzhauser Porzellanfabrik, Hertel Schwab & Co., Stutzhaus, near Ohrdruf, Thüringia, Germany

Date: 1910

Material: Bisque heads to be used on composition, cloth or leather bodies, all-bisque dolls, pincushion dolls

Mark:

Made in Germany 757/2

152 4

Marked Character Baby: Perfect bisque head, molded and painted hair or good wig, sleep or painted eyes, open or open/closed mouth with molded tongue; bent limb baby body; dressed; all in good condition.

#130, 142, 150, 151, 152:

11—12in	(28—31cm)	**$300—350**
16—18in	(41—46cm)	**450—500**
20—22in	(51—56cm)	**600—650**
24—25in	(61—64cm)	**750—850**

14in (36cm) 150 character baby. *Private Collection.*

12in (31cm) 152 character baby. *H&J Foulke, Inc.*

Hertel, Schwab & Co. continued

Marked Character Child: Perfect bisque head, painted or sleeping eyes, closed mouth; jointed composition body; dressed; all in good condition.

#134, 149, 141: 16—18in (41-46cm)   **$4500—5000**
#154 (closed mouth): 16—17in (41-43cm)   **2000—2200**
#154 (open mouth): 20in (51cm) toddler   **1200—1300**
#169: 19—21in (48—53cm) toddler   **3000—3500****

**Not enough price samples to compute a reliable range.

All-Bisque Doll: Jointed shoulders and hips; good wig, glass eyes, closed or open mouth; molded and painted shoes and stockings; undressed; all in good condition. Mold *#208.*

4—5in (10—13cm)   **$185—225***
7in (18cm)   **325—365***
8in (20cm)   **425—475***
Swivel neck, 6—7in (15—18cm)   **375—425**

*This is for fine quality bisque, lovely tinting. Do not pay these prices for mediocre dolls.

16in (41cm) 134 character child. *Jackie Kaner.*

4½in (12cm) 208 all-bisque girl. *H&J Foulke, Inc.*

Hertel, Schwab & Co. continued

Marked Googly: Perfect bisque head, large glass side-glancing sleeping eyes, wig or molded hair, impish closed mouth; composition body; cute clothes; all in good condition.

#165:

11in (28cm) baby	**$2500—2800**	
15in (38cm) toddler	**3500—4000**	

#163:

12in (31cm) baby	**2500—2800**	
16in (41cm) toddler	**4000—4200**	

#172, 173:

15—16in (38—41cm)	**4500—5500****	

**Not enough price samples to compute a reliable range.

16in (41cm) 163 googly. *Jackie Kaner.*

Hertwig & Co.

Maker: Hertwig & Co., porcelain factory, Katzhutte, Thüringia, Germany
Date: 1864—on
Material: China and bisque shoulder heads, all-bisque dolls, half-bisque dolls
Mark: Germany

Bisque Shoulder Heads with Molded Bonnets: Ca. 1880—1920. Bisque head with molded hair and bonnet, painted facial features; old cloth body with bisque limbs; old clothes; good condition.
12—15in (31—38cm) "Margueritas" **$200—250**

Pet Name China Heads: Ca. 1905. China shoulder head, molded yoke with name in gold; black or blonde painted hair (one-third were blonde), blue painted eyes; old cloth body (some with alphabet or other figures printed on cotton material), china limbs; properly dressed: all in good condition. Names such as ***Agnes, Bertha, Daisy, Dorothy, Edith, Esther, Ethel, Florence, Helen, Mabel, Marian*** and ***Pauline.*** Made for Butler Brothers, New York.

9—10in (23—25cm)	**$125—140**
14—16in (36—41cm)	**200—225**
19—21in (48—53cm)	**275—300**

4¼in (11cm) ***Dorothy*** china head. *H&J Foulke, Inc.*

12in (31cm) bisque shoulder head with molded butterfly bonnet. *Richard Wright Antiques.*

Hertwig & Co. continued

Half-Bisque Dolls: 1911. Head and body to waist of one-piece bisque, molded hair, painted features, bisque hands, lower legs with white stockings and molded shoes with heels and bows, other parts of body are cloth. Appropriate clothes; all in good condition.

4½in (12cm) **$200—225**
6½in (17cm) **275—300**

All-Bisque Children with Molded Clothes: 1900—1910. (See All-Bisque Section, page 43.)
Pink Bisque Characters: 1920. (See All-Bisque Section, page 47.)
All-Bisque Nodders: 1920. (See All-Bisque Section, page 51.)
Snow Babies: After 1910. (See Snow Babies Section, page 372.)

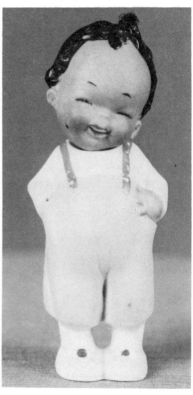

4in (10cm) nodder with brown complexion. *H&J Foulke, Inc.*

Half-bisque girl, original body and limbs. *H&J Foulke, Inc.*

Ernst Heubach

Maker: Ernst Heubach, porcelain factory, Köppelsdorf, Thüringia, Germany
Date: 1887—on
Material: Bisque head; kid, cloth or composition bodies
Mark: Heubach-Köppelsdorf
     250 - 15/o
     Germany

D.E.P. 1902

2/o

Heubach Child Doll: Ca. 1888—on. Perfect bisque head, good wig, sleep eyes, open mouth; kid, cloth or jointed composition body; dressed; all in good condition.

#275, kid or cloth body:
12—13in (31—33cm)	**$150—165**	
16—18in (41—46cm)	**210—250**	
21—23in (53—58cm)	**300—350**	

#250, composition body:
8—9in (20—23cm)	**140—165**	
13—15in (33—38cm)	**225—275**	
18—20in (46—51cm)	**325—375**	
23—24in (58—61cm)	**400—450**	
28in (71cm)	**525—550**	

Painted bisque, *#250*,
7—8in (18—20cm)	**90—100**

23in (58cm) mold 250 child. *Dolly Valk Collection.*

Character Baby: 1910—on. Perfect bisque head, good wig, sleep eyes, open mouth (sometimes also wobbly tongue and pierced nostrils); composition bent-limb baby or toddler body; dressed; all in good condition.

#300, 320, 342 and others:
6in (15cm)	**$225**
9—11in (23—28cm)	**250—300**
14—16in (36—41cm)	**375—400**
19—21in (48—53cm)	**475—525**
24in (61cm)	**600**

#320, jointed composition body, **750**
  28in (71cm)

Toddler:
9in (23cm) 5 piece body	**275—325**
13—14in (33—36cm)	**450—500**
23—25in (58—64cm)	**750—850**

Painted Bisque:
10in (25cm) toddler	**225**
12in (31cm) baby	**225**
#417 toddler, 11in (28cm)	**600**

20in (51cm) mold 317 character baby. *H&J Foulke, Inc.*

Ernst Heubach continued

Character Children: 1910—on. Perfect bisque shoulder head with molded hair in various styles, some with hair bows, painted eyes, open/closed mouth; cloth body with composition lower arms.

#262 and others:

   12in (31cm) **$375—425****

**Not enough price samples to compute a reliable range.

Infant: Ca. 1925. Perfect bisque head, molded and painted hair, sleep eyes, closed mouth; cloth body, composition or celluloid hands, appropriate clothes; all in good condition. (For photographs see *6th Blue Book*, page 200 and *5th Blue Book*, page 177.)

#349, 339, 350: 10—12in (25—31cm) **$450—550****

#338, 340: 14—16in (36—41cm)   **700—800****

**Not enough price samples to compute a reliable range.

Gypsy: Ca. late 1920s. Tan bisque head, matching toddler body; mohair wig, sleep eyes, open mouth with teeth, brass earrings; appropriate costume; all in good condition. (For photograph see *6th Blue Book*, page 200.)

#452:

   9—10in (23—25cm) **$275—325**

11in (28cm) shoulder head character child. *H&J Foulke, Inc.*

Gebrüder Heubach

Maker: Gebrüder Heubach, porcelain factory, Licht and Sonneberg, Thüringia, Germany

Date: 1820—on; doll heads 1910—on

Material: Bisque head, kid, cloth or jointed composition body or composition bent-limb body, all bisque

Mark:

Heubach Character Child: Ca. 1910. Perfect bisque head, molded hair, glass or intaglio eyes, closed or open/closed mouth, character face; jointed composition or kid body; dressed; all in good condition.

#5636 laughing child, glass eyes, 13—15in (33—38cm)   **$1350—1550**

#5689 smiling child (For photograph see *6th Blue Book*, page 197), 28—29in (71—74cm)   3000—4000

#5730 Santa, JCB, 32—34in (81—87cm)   3200—3400

#5777 Dolly Dimple, JCB, 19in (48cm)   2100—2300

#6969, 6970, 7246, 7407, 8017, 8420, pouty child, glass eyes, JCB:
  14in (36cm)   2000
  17in (43cm)   2350
  21in (53cm)   3000

#7550 o/c mouth, glass eyes, 14in (36cm)   900

#7622 and other socket head pouties, intaglio eyes, 15—17in (38—43cm)   900—1100

#7679 Whistler socket head, 14in (36cm)   1000

#7701, pouty, 19in (48cm) at auction   2550

#7788 Coquette, JCB, 14in (36cm)   950

#7852 molded coiled braids shoulder head, 15in (38cm)   2000

#7877, 7977 Baby Stuart socket head, 10—11in (25—28cm)   1000—1100

#7911, 8191 grinning, JCB, 15in (38cm)   900—1000

#8192, JCB:
  14—16in (36—41cm)   550—650
  18—22in (46—56cm)   850—950

#8590, 16in (41cm) at auction   3350

Shoulder heads, pouty or smiling, intaglio eyes, 14—15in (36—38cm)   400—450

#10586, 10633, JCB, 18—20in (46—51cm)   600—650

#11173 Tiss Me, 8in (20cm)   1000—1200**

**Not enough price samples to compute a reliable range.

See color photograph on page 80.

Gebrüder Heubach continued

12½in (32cm) 8590 character boy. *Richard Wright Antiques.*

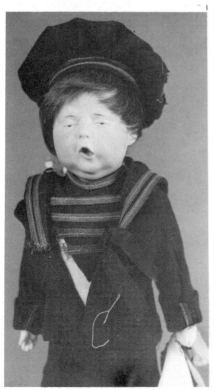

14in (36cm) 7246 pouty character. *Kay & Wayne Jensen Collection.*

14½in (37cm) 7448 character boy. *Richard Wright Antiques.*

Gebrüder Heubach continued

8in (20cm) 11173 character girl marketed by George Borgfeldt as *Tiss-Me*, 1927. *Esther Schwartz Collection.*

11½in (29cm) 7849 character boy shoulder head. *Yvonne Baird Collection.*

Gebrüder Heubach continued

All-Bisque:

Position Babies, 5in (13cm)	$300—350
Boy or Girl with bows or hair band:	
7—8in (18—20cm)	750—850
9in (23cm)	950
Bunny Boy or Girl, 5½in (14cm)	250—300
All-bisque boy or girl, 4in (10cm)	225—250
Chin-Chin character, 4in (10cm)	225—250
Action figures:	
6in (15cm)	275—325
4in (10cm)	150—175

See color photograph on page 113.

Heubach Babies: Ca. 1910. Perfect bisque head, molded hair, intaglio eyes, open or closed mouth, character face; composition bent-limb body; dressed; all in nice condition.

#6894, 7602, 6898 and other pouty babies:

6in (15cm)	$225—250
10in (25cm)	350—375
14in (36cm)	475—500
18in (46cm)	675—725
Shoulder head on kid body,	
12—14in (31—36cm)	350—400

#7604 laughing,
13—14in (33—36cm) 500—600

8½in (22cm) all-bisque character girl, all original. *Richard Wright Antiques.*

Horsman

Maker: E. I. Horsman Co., New York, N.Y., U.S.A. Also distributed dolls as a *verleger* for other manufacturers and imported French and German dolls.

Date: 1878—on

Billiken: 1909. Composition head with peak of hair at top of head, slanted slits for eyes, watermelon mouth; velvet or plush body; in very good condition.

    MARK: Cloth label on body; "Billiken" on right foot

12in (31cm) **$300—350**

Baby Bumps: 1910. Composition head with molded hair and painted features; stuffed cloth body. Good condition with some wear.

    MARK: None

12—14in (31—36cm) **$165—185**

Can't Break 'Em Characters: Ca. 1910. Heads and hands of "Can't Break 'Em" composition, hard stuffed cloth bodies with swivel joints at shoulders and hips; molded hair, painted eyes, character faces; appropriate clothes; all in good condition.

    MARK: "E.I.H.1911"

10—12in (25—31cm) **$125—150**

12in (31cm) *Billiken*, all original. *Private Collection.*

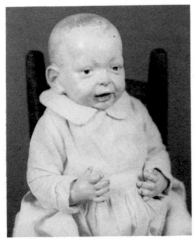

14in (36cm) *Baby Bumps. Betty Harms Collection.*

10in (25cm) *Can't Break 'Em*-type character. *H&J Foulke, Inc.*

Horsman continued

Gene Carr Character: 1916. Composition head with molded and painted hair, eyes painted open or closed, wide smiling mouth with teeth; cloth body with composition hands; original or appropriate clothes; all in good condition. Names such as: ***"Snowball"*** (Black Boy); ***"Mike"*** and ***"Jane"*** (eyes open); ***"Blink"*** and ***"Skinney"*** (eyes closed). Designed by Bernard Lipfert from Gene Carr's cartoon characters. (For photograph see *7th Blue Book*, page 210.)
MARK: None
13—14in (33—36cm) **$225—275**

Rosebud: 1920s. Composition swivel head, mohair wig, tin sleep eyes, open mouth with teeth, smiling face with dimples; cloth torso, composition arms and legs; original clothes; all in good condition. (For photograph see *4th Blue Book*, page 172.)
MARK: "ROSEBUD"
18—22in (46-56cm) **$200—250**

Mama Dolls: Ca. 1920—on. Composition head, cloth body, composition arms and lower legs; mohair wig or molded hair, sleep eyes; original clothes; all in very good condition.
MARK: "E. I. H. Co." or "HORSMAN"
12—14in (31—36cm) **$100—125**
18—20in (46—51cm) **125—150**

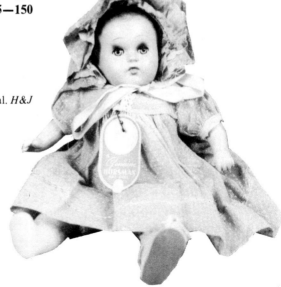

12in (31cm) mama doll, all original. *H&J Foulke, Inc.*

Horsman continued

Jackie Coogan: 1921. Composition head with molded hair, painted eyes, closed mouth; cloth torso with composition hands; appropriate clothes; all in good condition.

MARK: "E. I. H. Co. 19 © 21"

14in (36cm) **$450—500**

Marked Tynie Baby: 1924. Solid dome infant head with sleep eyes, closed mouth, slightly frowning face; cloth body with composition arms; appropriate clothes; all in good condition. Designed by Bernard Lipfert. (For photograph see *6th Blue Book*, page 204.)

MARK: © 1924
E.I. Horsman Inc.
Made in
Germany

Bisque head,
 12in (31cm) h.c.   **$ 650**
Composition head,
 15in (38cm) long   **250—275**
All-bisque with swivel neck, glass eyes, wigged or solid dome head,
 9—10in (23—25cm)   **1200—1300**

HEbee-SHEbee: 1925. All-composition, jointed at shoulders and hips, painted eyes, molded white chemise and real ribbon or wool ties in molded shoes; all in good condition. Blue shoes indicate a *HEbee,* pink ones a *SHEbee.* (For photograph see *7th Blue Book*, page 212.)

11in (28cm) **$425—475**

14in (36cm) *Jackie Coogan*, all original. *Miriam Blankman Collection.*

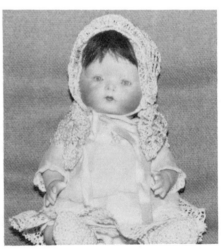

All-bisque *Tynie Baby. Courtesy of Sandra Pipes.*

Horsman continued

Ella Cinders: 1925. Composition head with molded hair, painted eyes; cloth body with composition arms and lower legs; original clothes; all in fair condition. From the comic strip by Bill Conselman and Charlie Plumb, for the Metropolitan Newspaper Service.

MARK: "1925 © MNS"

18in (46cm) **$500**

Baby Dimples: 1928. Composition head with molded and painted hair, tin sleep eyes, open mouth, smiling face; soft cloth body with composition arms and legs; original or appropriate old clothes; all in good condition. (For photograph see *7th Blue Book*, page 212.)

MARK: " ©
        E. I. H. CO. INC."

16—18in (41—46cm)   **$165—185**
22—24in (56—61cm)   **225—250**

Child Dolls: Ca. 1930s and 1940s. All-composition with swivel neck, shoulders and hips; mohair wig, sleep eyes; original clothes; all in good condition.

MARK: "HORSMAN"

13—14in (33—36cm)	**$125—150**
16—18in (41—46cm)	**165—185**
Chubby Toddler, 16—18in (41—46cm)	**165—185**

18in (46cm) ***Ella Cinders***, all original. *H&J Foulke, Inc.*

13in (33cm) all-composition child, all original and boxed. *Miriam Blankman Collection.*

Horsman continued

Jeanie: Ca. 1937. All-composition with swivel neck, shoulders and hips; molded and painted hair with peak on top, sleep eyes, closed mouth; appropriate old clothes; all in good condition.

MARK: "JEANIE
            HORSMAN"

14in (36cm) **$135—160**

Jo-Jo: 1937. All-composition toddler with swivel neck, shoulders and hips; mohair wig with braids, sleep eyes, closed mouth; appropriate old clothing; all in good condition. (For photograph see *7th Blue Book*, page 213.)

MARK: © JO-JO
            1937 HORSMAN

12½in (32cm) **$150—165**

14in (36cm) ***Jeanie***, re-dressed. *Miriam Blankman Collection.*

Mary Hoyer

Maker: The Mary Hoyer Doll Mfg. Co., Reading, PA., U.S.A.
Date: Ca. 1925—on
Material: First all-composition, later all-hard plastic
Size: 14 and 18in (36 and 46cm)
Mark: Embossed on torso:

"The
Mary Hoyer
Doll"

or in a circle:

"ORIGINAL
Mary Hoyer
Doll"

Marked Mary Hoyer: Material as above; swivel neck; jointed shoulders and hips, original wig, sleep eyes with eyelashes, closed mouth; all in excellent condition. Original tagged factory clothes or garments made at home from Mary Hoyer patterns.

Composition, 14in (36cm)	**$300—350**
Hard plastic, 14in (36cm)	**325—375**

14in (36cm) Mary Hoyer, original crocheted clothes. *Esther Schwartz Collection.*

Huret

Maker: Maison Huret, Paris, France

Date: 1850—on

Material: China or bisque heads; kid or wood jointed bodies, sometimes with pewter hands and feet

Mark: "Huret" or "Maison Huret" stamped on body

Marked Huret Doll: China or bisque shoulder head, good wig, painted or glass eyes, closed mouth; kid body; beautifully dressed; all in good condition.

16—19in (41—48cm)   **$5000 up**

Wood body, 16—19in (41—48cm)   **7000 up**

Gutta Percha body, 16—19in (41—48cm) **8000 up**

17in (43cm) Huret-type china shoulder head with glass eyes.

Ideal

Maker: Ideal Novelty and Toy Co., Brooklyn, N.Y., U.S.A.
Date: 1907—on.

Uneeda Kid: 1914—1919. Composition head with molded brown hair, blue painted eyes, closed mouth; cloth body with composition arms and legs with molded black boots; original bloomer suit, yellow slicker and rain hat; carrying a box of Uneeda Biscuits; all in good condition, showing some wear. (For photograph see *6th Blue Book*, page 209.)

16in (41cm)	**$275—300**
Molded hat	**325—375**

Snoozie: 1933. Composition head, character expression with yawning mouth, sleeping eyes, molded hair, composition arms and legs or rubber arms, cloth body; baby clothes; all in good condition. 13, 16 and 20in (33, 41 and 51cm). (For photograph see *7th Blue Book*, page 216.)

MARK: ©
 By B. LIPFERT

16—20in (41—51cm) **$150—175**

Shirley Temple: 1935. For detailed information see pages 361 to 363.

Mama Doll: Ca. 1920—on. Composition head, cloth body, composition arms and lower legs; mohair wig or molded hair, sleep eyes; appropriate old clothes; all in very good condition.

MARK:

14—16in (36—41cm) **$125—150**

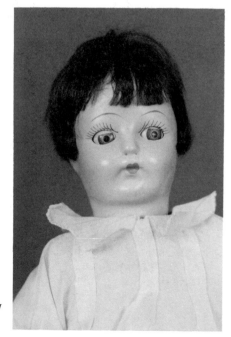

13in (33cm) Ideal mama doll. *H&J Foulke, Inc.*

Ideal continued

Betsy Wetsy: 1937—on. Composition head with molded hair, sleep eyes; soft rubber body jointed at neck, shoulders and hips; drinks, wets; appropriate clothes; all in good condition. This doll went through many changes including hard plastic head on rubber body, later vinyl body, later completely vinyl. Various sizes.
MARK: "IDEAL"
14—16in (36—41cm) rubber body   **$90—110**

Snow White: 1937. All-composition, jointed at neck, shoulders and hips; black mohair wig, lashed sleep eyes, open mouth; original dress with velvet bodice and cape, and rayon skirt with figures of seven dwarfs; in good condition. 11in (28cm), 13in (33cm) and 18in (46cm) sizes. (For photograph see *Doll Classics*, page 190.)
MARK: On body:
"SHIRLEY TEMPLE/18"
On dress: "An Ideal Doll"
11—13in (28—33cm)   **$425—450**
18in (46cm)   **425—450**
Molded black hair, painted blue bow, painted eyes,
13—14in (33—36cm) **150—175**

Betty Jane: 1943. All-composition ***Shirley Temple***-type doll with jointed neck, shoulders and hips; lashed sleeping eyes (sometimes flirty), open mouth with teeth; all original; very good condition. (For photograph see *7th Blue Book*, page 217.)
MARK: IDEAL
18
18in (46cm)   **$200—225**

Flirty-eyed Baby: 1938. Composition head, lower arms and legs, cloth body; flirty eyes, closed mouth, molded hair; original clothing; all in good condition.
MARK: "IDEAL DOLL"
16—18in (41—46cm)   **$150—175**

16in (41cm) flirty-eyed baby, all original.
H&J Foulke, Inc.

Ideal continued

Deanna Durbin: 1938. All-composition, jointed at neck, shoulders and hips; original human hair or mohair wig, sleep eyes, smiling mouth with teeth; original clothing; all in good condition. Various sizes.

MARK: Metal button with picture:
"DEANNA DURBIN, IDEAL DOLL, U.S.A."

14in (36cm)	**$350—400**
20—21in (51—53cm)	**500—550**
24—25in (61—64cm)	**650**

Judy Garland as Dorothy of the Wizard of Oz: 1939. All-composition, jointed at neck, shoulders and hips; dark human hair wig, dark sleep eyes, open mouth with teeth; original dress; all in good condition. (For photograph see *4th Blue Book*, page 178.)

MARK: On head and body: "IDEAL DOLL"
16in (41cm) **$1000 up**

21in (53cm) ***Deanna Durbin***, all original. *H&J Foulke, Inc.*

Ideal continued

Flexy Dolls: 1938—on. Head, hands and feet of composition; arms and legs of flexible metal cable, torso of wire mesh; in original clothes; all in good condition.

MARK: On head: "Ideal Doll"

12in (31cm)

Baby Snooks (Fanny Brice)	**$225—250**
Mortimer Snerd	**225—250**
Soldier	**150—200**
Children	**150—175**

Composition and wood segmented characters: 1940. Molded composition heads with painted features, wood segmented bodies. Label on front torso gives name of character.

Pinocchio, 10½in (27cm)	**$225—250**
King-Little, 14in (36cm)	**200—225**
Jiminy Cricket, 9in (23cm)	**200—225**

Magic Skin Baby: 1940. Composition head with molded hair (later babies had hard plastic heads), sleep eyes, closed mouth; stuffed latex rubber body, jointed shoulders and hips; appropriate clothes; all in good condition. Various sizes. (For photograph see *7th Blue Book*, page 219.)

MARK: On head: "IDEAL"

14—15in (36—38cm)   **$75—85**

12in (31cm) *Mortimer Snerd*, all original.
H&J Foulke, Inc.

9in (23cm) *Jiminy Cricket*, all original.
Private Collection.

Ideal continued

Brother Coos: 1948—1952. Hard plastic head with dark molded hair, sleep eyes, closed mouth; composition arms and legs, cloth body; dressed; all in good condition. Sounds like a baby when squeezed.

MARK: Ideal Doll
            Made in U.S.A.

25—30in (64—77cm)   **$125—150**

Baby Coos in sizes 14—30in (36—77cm) with Magic Skin body,
    14—16in (36—41cm)   **65—85**

Toni and P-90 and P-91 Family: 1948—on. Series of girl dolls. Most were completely of hard plastic with jointed neck, shoulders and hips, nylon wig, sleep eyes, closed mouth; original clothes; all in excellent condition. Various sizes, but most are 14in (36cm).

MARK: On head: "IDEAL DOLL"
            On body: "IDEAL DOLL
                        P-90
                        Made in USA"

14in (36cm) **Baby Coos**, all original and boxed. *H&J Foulke, Inc.*

Toni,
    14—15in (36—38cm)**$125—150**
    21in (53cm)   **250—275**
Mary Hartline,
    14in (36cm)   **150—165**
    22in (56cm)   **250—275**
Betsy McCall, vinyl head,
    14in (36cm)   **150—165**
Harriet Hubbard Ayer, vinyl head,
    14in (36m)   **150—165**
Miss Curity,
    14in (36cm)   **150—165**
Sara Ann,
    14in (36cm)   **150—165**

14in (36cm) **Toni**, all original. *H&J Foulke, Inc.*

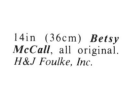

14in (36cm) **Betsy McCall**, all original. *H&J Foulke, Inc.*

Ideal continued

Saucy Walker: 1951. All-hard plastic, jointed at neck, shoulders and hips with walking mechanism; synthetic wig, flirty eyes, open mouth with tongue and teeth; original clothes; all in excellent condition.

MARK: "IDEAL DOLL"

16—17in (41—43cm) **$ 75—95**
20—22in (51—56cm)   **110—135**

Miss Revlon: 1955. Vinyl head with rooted hair, sleep eyes, closed mouth, earrings; hard plastic body with jointed waist and knees, high-heeled feet, vinyl arms with polished nails; original clothes; all in good condition. (For photograph see *6th Blue Book*, page 213.)

MARK: On head and body:
"IDEAL DOLL"

Miss Revlon, 17—19in (43—48cm) **$100—125**
Little Miss Revlon, 10½in (27cm)   **75—85**

Peter and Patty Playpal: 1960. Vinyl heads with rooted hair, sleep eyes; hard vinyl body, jointed at shoulders and hips; appropriate clothes; all in excellent condition. (For photograph see *7th Blue Book*, page 221.)

MARK: Peter: "IDEAL TOY CORP.
BE—35—38"
Patty: "IDEAL DOLL
G-35"

35—36in (89—91cm):
  Peter   **$300**
  Patty   **250**
18in (46cm)
  Patty   **100—125**
42in (107cm)
  Daddy's Girl   775

22in (56cm) *Saucy Walker*, replaced dress. *Miriam Blankman Collection.*

Italian Bisque

Maker: Ceramica Furga of Canneto sull'Oglio, Mantua, Italy, and others
Date: Ca. 1910—on for those shown here
Material: Bisque head, composition body sometimes with cardboard torso
Mark:

"Furga
Canneto & Oglio"   or $\mathcal{J}$taly
I/6

Marked Italian Bisque Doll: Perfect bisque dolly-face head with suitable wig, painted eyebrows and eyelashes, glass eyes, closed or open mouth with teeth; composition body (some quite crude); dressed; all in good condition.

Closed mouth,
   7—8in (18—20cm) **$225—250**
Open mouth,
   14—16in (36—41cm) **275—325****
   24in (61cm)   **750—850****

**Not enough price samples to compute a reliable range.

7in (18cm) marked "Italy" doll, all original. *H&J Foulke, Inc.*

Italian Hard Plastic

Maker: Bonomi, Ottolini, Ratti, Furga and other Italian firms
Date: Later 1940s and 1950s
Material: Heavy hard plastic, sometimes painted, or plastic coated papier-mâché
Mark: Usually a wrist tag; company name on head

Italian Hard Plastic: Heavy, fine quality material jointed at shoulders and hips; human hair wig, sleep eyes, sometimes flirty, often a character face; original clothes; all in excellent condition.

15—17in (38—43cm) **$ 90—110**
19—21in (48—53cm)   **125—150**

See color photograph on page 114.

21in (53cm) *Sympatica* by Ottolini. *H&J Foulke, Inc.*

Japanese Bisque Caucasian Dolls

Maker: Various Japanese firms; heads were imported by New York importers, such as Morimura Brothers, Yamato Importing Co. and others.

Date: 1915—on

Material: Bisque head, composition body

Mark: Morimura Brothers

Various other marks with Japan
or Nippon, such as J. W., F. Y., and others

Character Baby: Perfect bisque socket head with solid dome or wig, glass eyes, open mouth with teeth, dimples; composition bent-limb baby body; dressed; all in good condition.

9—10in (23—25cm)	**$125—150***
14—15in (36—38cm)	**225—275***
20—22in (51—56cm)	**425—475***

Child Doll: Perfect bisque head, mohair wig, glass sleep eyes, open mouth; jointed composition or kid body; dressed; all in good condition.

14—16in (36—41cm)	**$225—250***
20—22in (51—56cm)	**300—350***

*Do not pay as much for doll with inferior bisque head.

10in (25cm) Morimura Brothers *My Darling* character baby. *H&J Foulke, Inc.*

Jullien

Maker: Jullien, Jeune of Paris, France
Date: 1875—1904 when joined with S.F.B.J.
Material: Bisque head, composition and wood body
Mark: "JULLIEN" with size number

JuLLiEN
1

Marked Jullien Bébé: Bisque head, lovely wig, paperweight eyes, closed
mouth, pierced ears; jointed wood and composition body; pretty old clothes;
all in good condition. (For photograph see *5th Blue Book*, page 196.)

17—19in (43—48cm)	**$3100—3400**
24—26in (61—66cm)	**3900—4500**
Open mouth, 23—24in (58—61cm)	**2200—2400**

24in (61cm) Jullien, walking body. *H&J Foulke, Inc.*

Jumeau

Maker: Maison Jumeau, Paris, France
Date: 1842—on
Material: Bisque head, kid or composition body
Trademark: Bébé Jumeau (1886)
              Bébé Prodige (1886)
              Bébé Francais (1896)

Fashion Lady: Late 1860s—on. Usually marked with number only on head, blue stamp on body. Perfect bisque swivel head on shoulder plate, old wig, paperweight eyes, closed mouth, pierced ears; all-kid body or kid with bisque lower arms and legs or cloth Lacmann body with leather arms; appropriate old clothes; all in good condition.

MARK:

JUMEAU
MEDAILLE D'OR
PARIS

12—13in (31—33cm)	$ 2500—3000*	
18—20in (46—51cm)	3500—4000*	
25—27in (64—69cm)	5000—6000*	
30in (76cm)	7500	
34—36in (86—91cm)	11,000—15,000	
Wood body,		
36in (91cm)	22,000**	

*Add 25% for original wig and clothing.
**Not enough price samples to complete a reliable range.

18in (46cm) Jumeau fashion doll, all original. See color photograph on page 115. *Yvonne Baird Collection.*

Jumeau continued

Long-Face Triste Bébé: Ca. 1870s. Usually marked with number only on head, blue stamp on body. Perfect bisque socket head with beautiful wig, blown glass eyes, closed mouth, applied pierced ears; jointed composition body with straight wrists; lovely clothes; all in good condition.

20—22in (51—56cm) **$16,000**
24—27in (61—69cm) **18,000 up**

Long-face Triste Bébé. (For color photograph see page 117.) *Yvonne Baird Collection.*

Early Almond—Eyed Bébé (so-called Portrait Jumeau): Ca. 1870s. Usually marked with size number only on head, blue stamp on body; skin or other good wig; unusually large paperweight eyes, closed mouth, pierced ears; jointed composition body with straight wrists; nicely dressed; all in good condition.

15—17in (38—43cm) **$5000—5500**
23—26in (58—66cm) **7000—8000**

23½in (60cm) early almond-eyed portrait Jumeau. (See color photograph on page 116.) *Yvonne Baird Collection.*

Jumeau continued

E. J. Bébé: Ca. 1880. Head incised as below, blue stamp on body. Perfect bisque socket head with good wig, paperweight eyes, closed mouth, pierced ears; jointed composition body with straight wrists; lovely clothes; all in good condition.

MARK: On head: DÉPOSÉ E. 7 J.

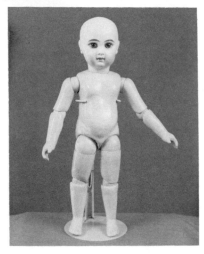

10in (25cm) #1	$ 4800*
14—15in (36—38cm)	5200—5600*
20—22in (51—56cm)	6300—6900*
26—28in (61—71cm)	7500—8500*

EJA,
26in (66cm)	**10,000**

*Tête-style face slightly lower.

15in (38cm) E.J. bebe. *Yvonne Baird Collection.*

See color photograph on page 115.

Incised Jumeau Depose Bébé: Ca. 1880. Head incised as below, blue stamp on body. Perfect bisque socket head with good wig, paperweight eyes, closed mouth, pierced ears; jointed composition body with straight wrists; lovely clothes; all in good condition.

MARK: Incised on head: "JUMEAU DEPOSE"

10in (25cm) #1	$4000—4300
11—13in (28—33cm)	4300—4800
18—20in (46—51cm)	5000—5500
26—27in (66—69cm)	6500—7000

21in (53cm) incised Jumeau Bébé. *Esther Schwartz Collection.*

Jumeau continued

Tête Jumeau Bébé: 1879—1899, then through S.F.B.J. Red stamp on head as indicated below, blue stamp or "Bebe Jumeau" oval sticker on body. Perfect bisque head, original or good French wig, beautiful stationary eyes, closed mouth, pierced ears; jointed composition body with jointed or straight wrists; original or lovely clothes; all in good condition.

MARK:

DÉPOSÉ
TETE JUMEAU
B^TE SGDG
6

10in (25cm) #1	**$3000—3500***
12—13in (31—33cm)	**2000—2400***
15—16in (38—41cm)	**2500—2800***
18—20in (46—51cm)	**3100—3400***
21—23in (53—58cm)	**3400—3800***
25—27in (64—69cm)	**3900—4500***
31—33in (79—84cm)	**5500—6500***
Lady body, 20in (51cm)	**5000—5500***
Open mouth:	
14—16in (36—41cm)	**1400—1600**
20—22in (51—56cm)	**2000—2200**
24—25in (61—64cm)	**2400—2500**
32—34in (81—86cm)	**3200—3400**

*Allow more for an especially fine example.

See color photograph on page 116.

32in (81cm) Tête Jumeau. *Kay & Wayne Jensen Collection.*

Jumeau continued

#230 Character Child: Ca. 1910.
Perfect bisque socket head, open
mouth, set or sleep eyes, good
wig; jointed composition body:
dressed; all in good condition.
13in (33cm)   **$1250**
21—23in (53—58cm)   **1800—2000**

#1907 Jumeau Child: Ca. 1900.
Sometimes red-stamped "Tete
Jumeau." Perfect bisque head,
good quality wig, set or sleep
eyes, open mouth, pierced ears;
jointed composition body; nicely
dressed; all in good condition.
16—18in (41—46cm)   **$1400—1600**
24—25in(61—64cm)   **2000—2200**
33—34in (84—87cm)   **3000—3300**

Jumeau Great Ladies: Ca. 1940s.
Perfect bisque socket head with
adult features, fancy mohair wig,
fixed eyes, closed mouth; five-
piece composition body with
painted black slippers, metal
stand attached to foot; a series of
ladies dressed in fancy costumes;
all original; in excellent condition. (For photograph see *Doll
Classics*, page 25.)
MARK: "221" on head
10—11in (25—28cm)   **$500—550**

Princess Elizabeth Jumeau: 1938
through S.F.B.J. Perfect bisque
socket head highly colored, good
wig, glass flirty eyes, closed
mouth; jointed composition
body; dressed; all in good condi-

22in (56cm) 1907 Tête Jumeau. *Private
Collection.*

MARK: 71   UNIS
                    FRANCE   149
                    306
                    JUMEAU
                    1938
                    PARIS

Body Incised: JUMEAU
                    PARIS
                    Princess

18—19in (46—48cm)   **$1100—1300**
32—33in (81—84cm)   **2400**

K & K

Maker: K & K Toy Co., New York, N.Y., U.S.A.
Date: 1915—on
Material: Bisque or composition head; cloth and composition body
Mark: Size numbers 45, 56 and 60   *Germany*
                                         K & K
                                         60
                                         Thuringia

K & K Character Child: Perfect bisque shoulder head, mohair wig, sleep eyes, open mouth with teeth; cloth body with composition arms and legs or leather legs; appropriate clothes; all in good condition.

18—20in (46—51cm)   **$375—425**
Composition head, 18—20in (46—51cm), all original   **175—200**

20in (51cm) ***K & K*** character child. *H&J Foulke, Inc.*

Kamkins

Maker: Louise R. Kampes Studios, Atlantic City, N.J., U.S.A.

Date: 1919—on

Material: Molded mask face, cloth stuffed torso and limbs

Size: About 16—19in (41—48cm)

Mark: Red paper heart on left side of chest:

Also sometimes stamped with black on foot or back of head:

KAMKINS

A DOLLY MADE TO LOVE
PATENTED BY L.R. KAMPES
ATLANTIC CITY,   N.J.

KAMKINS
A DOLLY MADE TO LOVE
_ PATENTED _
FROM
L.R. KAMPES
ATLANTIC CITY
N.J.

Marked Kamkins: Molded mask face with painted features, wig; cloth body and limbs; original clothing; all in excellent condition.

18—20in (46—51cm) **$1100—1200**

Fair to good condition **650—750**

19in (48cm) *Kamkins*, replaced clothing. *Dolly Valk Collection.*

Kämmer & Reinhardt

Maker: Kämmer & Reinhardt of Waltershausen, Thüringia, Germany
Heads often by Simon & Halbig

Date: 1886—on

Material: Bisque socket head, composition body, later papier-mâché, rubber
or celluloid heads, composition bodies

Size: 5½ to 42in (14 to 107cm)

Trademarks: Magestic Doll, Mein Liebling (My Darling), Der Schelm (The
Flirt), Die Kokette (The Coquette)

Mark: In 1895 began using K(star)R, sometimes with "S & H." Mold number
for bisque socket head begins with a 1; for papier-mâché, 9; for
celluloid, 7. Size number is height in centimeters. K $\bigstar$ R

$$SIMON \;\& \;HALBIG$$
$$116/A$$
$$\underline{50}$$

Child Doll: 1886—1895. Perfect bisque head, original or good wig, sleep or set
eyes, closed mouth, pierced ears; ball-jointed composition body; dressed; all
in good condition.

#192:

16—18in (41—46cm)	**$1400—1700**
23—25in (58—64cm)	**2100—2300**

Open mouth:

7—8in (18—20cm)	**350—400**
14—16in (36—41cm)	**500—600**
19—21in (48—53cm)	**725—775**
25—27in (64—69cm)	**1000—1250**

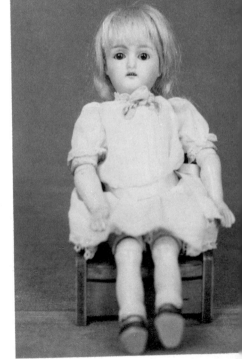

8in (20cm) 192 child. *Private Collection.*

Kämmer & Reinhardt continued

Child Doll: 1895—1930s. Perfect bisque head, original or good wig, sleep eyes, open mouth, pierced ears; dressed; ball-jointed composition body; all in good condition.

#403 or no number:

13—14in (33—36cm)	**$ 400—450***
16—17in (41—43cm)	**500—550***
19—21in (48—53cm)	**600—700***
23—25in (58—64cm)	**700—800***
29—31in (74—79cm)	**1000—1100***
35—36in (89—91cm)	**1700—1900**
39—42in (99—107cm)	**2500 up**

*Allow $50 additional for flirty eyes.

32in (81cm) K★R flirty child. *Leone McMullen Collection.*

6½in (17cm) K★R tiny child walker. *H&J Foulke, Inc.*

Tiny Child Doll: Perfect bisque head, mohair wig, sleep eyes, open mouth; five-piece composition body with molded and painted shoes and socks.

6—7in (15—18cm)	**$325—375**
8—9in (20—23cm)	**375—400**
Walker,	
6—7in (15—18cm)	**375—400**
Closed mouth,	
6in (15cm)	**375—400**
Jonted body,	
8—10in (20—25cm)	**425—475**

Baby #100 (so-called Kaiser Baby): 1909. Perfect bisque solid-dome head, original composition bent-limb body; painted eyes, open/closed mouth; dressed all in good condition. (For photograph see page 14.)

10—11in (25—28cm)	**$ 400—450**
14—16in (36—41cm)	**550—650**
20—21in (51—53cm)	**900—1000**
Glass eyes (unmarked), 17—18in (43—46cm)	**2000—2400**
Black or brown, 11in (28cm)	**650—750**

Kämmer & Reinhardt continued

Character Babies or Toddlers: 1914—on. Perfect bisque head, original or good wig, sleep eyes, open mouth; composition bent-limb or jointed toddler body; nicely dressed; may have voice box or spring tongue; all in good condition. (See *Simon & Halbig Dolls, The Artful Aspect* for photographs of mold numbers not pictured here.)

#126, 22, 26 Baby:

10—12in (25—31cm)	$ 375—425
17—19in (43—48cm)	550—650*
23—25in (58—64cm)	800—900*
30—33in (76—84cm)	1800—2100

#126, 22 Toddler:

6—7in (15—18cm)	375—425
12—14in (31—36cm)	600—650*
19—21in (48—53cm)	850—950*
24—25in (61—64cm)	1200—1300
28—30in (71—76cm)	1650—1850

#126 Child:

24in (61cm)	750

#121 Baby:

14—16in (36—41cm)	600—700
23—24in (58—61cm)	1000—1100

#122, 128 Baby:

11—12in (28—31cm)	425—475
17—19in (43—48cm)	800—900
23—25in (58—64cm)	1200—1600
30in (76cm)	2500

#121, 122, 128 Toddler:

14—16in (36—41cm)	1000—1100
21—23in (53—58cm)	1500—1650
30—32in (76—81cm)	2500

#118A Baby:

18—20in (46—51cm)	1600—1800**

#119 Baby:

24in (61cm) at auction	4900**

#135 Baby:

20in (51cm)	1600—1800**

#135 Child:

15in (38cm)	1000**

Composition Head ***#926***:

23in (58cm) five-piece toddler body	450—500

*Allow $50 additional for flirty eyes.

**Not enough price samples to compute a reliable range.

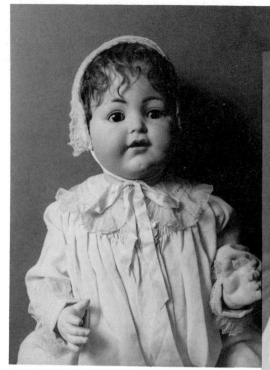

30in (76cm) K★R 128 character baby.
H&J Foulke, Inc.

11in (28cm) K★R 22 character baby.
H&J Foulke, Inc.

20in (51cm) K★R 126 character baby, all
original. *Leone McMullen Collection.*

Kämmer & Reinhardt continued

Character Children: 1909—on. Perfect bisque socket head, good wig, painted or glass eyes, closed mouth; composition ball-jointed body; nicely dressed; all in good condition. (See *Simon & Halbig, The Artful Aspect* for photographs of mold numbers not pictured here.)

#101:

7in (18cm) five-piece body	$ 950—1000
7—8in (18—20cm) jointed body	1100—1250
18—20in (46—51cm)	2800—3000
Glass eyes, 16in (41cm)	4200**

#102:

12in (31cm)	9500**

#103, 104:

18—20in (46—51cm)	30,000**

#106:

22in (56cm) at auction	36,300**

#107:

22in (55cm)	16,000**

#109:

16—18in (41—46cm)	7000—8000
21in (53cm)	10,000 up

**Not enough price samples to compute a reliable range.

18in (46cm) K★R 101 character girl. *Private Collection.*

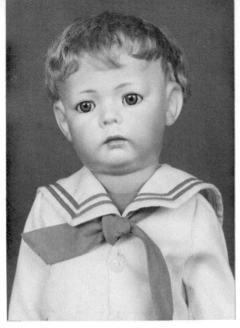

22in (56cm) K★R 115A toddler. *Private Collection.*

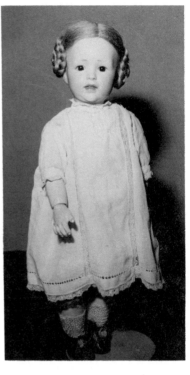

12in (31cm) K★R 112 character girl with glass eyes. *Jackie Kaner.*

#112, 112x:
16—18in (41—46cm)	**7500—8500**
24in (61cm)	**12,000**
Glass eyes, 16in (41cm)	**8000 up****

#114: (See page 16 for photograph.)
7in (18cm) five-piece body	**1100—1150**
10—11in (25—28cm)	**2000—2300**
17—19in (43—48cm)	**4000—4500**
24in (61cm)	**5500—6000**
Glass eyes, 17in (43cm)	**5500****

#115, 115A:
Baby, 11—12in (28—31cm)	**1800—2000***
Toddler, 16—18in (41—46cm)	**3700—4200***
25in (64cm)	**6000***

#116, 116A, open/closed mouth:
Baby, 14—16in (36—41cm)	**1750—2000***
Toddler, 16—17in (36—41cm)	**2450—2650***

*Allow additional for molded hair.

**Not enough price samples to compute a reliable range.

Kämmer & Reinhardt continued

#116A, open mouth:

Baby, 14—16in (36—41cm)	**1500—1800**
Toddler, 18—21in (46—53cm)	**2300—2600**

#117, 117A, closed mouth:

12—14in (31—36cm)	**2750—3250**
18—20in (46—51cm)	**4250—4850**
23—25in (59—64cm)	**5500—6000**
28—30in (71—76cm)	**6500—7500**

#117n, sleep eyes:

14—16in (36—41cm)	**850—950**

#117n, flirty eyes:

14—16in (36—41cm)	**1000—1200**
20—22in (51—56cm)	**1600—1800**
33—36in (84—91cm)	**2700—3000**

15in (38cm) K★R 117 **Mein Liebling**.
Private Collection.

17½in (45cm) K★R 117n character child.
Private Collection.

Kämmer & Reinhardt continued

#123, 124:
  17in (43cm)   10,000**

#127:
  Baby, 14—15in (36—38cm)   1000
  23—25in (59—64cm)   1800—2000
  Toddler or child, 13in (33cm)   1000
  Toddler, 27in (69cm)   2200

**Not enough price samples to compute a reliable range.

Infant: 1924—on. Perfect bisque head, molded and painted hair, glass eyes, open mouth; pink cloth body, composition hands; nicely dressed; all in good condition.
14in (36cm)   **$1100—1200**

22in (56cm) K★R 116A character toddler.
Private Collection.

17in (43cm) K★R 112 character boy.
Esther Schwartz Collection.

Kestner

Maker: J. D. Kestner, Jr., doll factory, Waltershausen, Thüringia, Germany.
Kestner & Co., porcelain factory, Ohrdruf.

Date: 1816—on

Material: Bisque heads, kid or composition bodies, bodies on tiny dolls are
jointed at the knee, but not the elbow, all bisque

Size: Up to 42in (107cm)

***Child doll, closed mouth, socket
head:*** Ca. 1880. Perfect bisque
head, plaster dome, good wig,
paperweight or sleep eyes, closed
mouth; composition ball-jointed
body with straight wrists; well
dressed; all in good condition.
Some marked with size number
only.

#169, 128, and
unmarked pouty face:
12—14in (31—36cm)$1450—1650
17—19in (43—48cm) 1950—2150
23—25in (58—64cm) 2550—2750

#XI and very pouty face:
14—16in (36—41cm) 2150—2350
19—21in (48—53cm) 2550—2650
24—25in (61—64cm) 2850—3150

A.T.-type (For photograph
see *7th Blue Book*, page 242.):
20in (51cm)   4200—4500
Open mouth,
19in (48cm)   2200

Bru-type, molded teeth,
jointed ankles:
16—18in (41—46cm) 3000

Open mouth, square cut teeth:
10—11in (25—28cm)   425—475
14—16in (36—41cm)   600—700

TOP RIGHT: 11in (28cm) closed mouth
child incised "5." (See color photograph
on page 120.) *Private Collection.*

MIDDLE: 16in (41cm) closed mouth
child incised "10." *Private Collection.*

15½in (39cm) Bru-type Kestner, open/
closed mouth with molded teeth. *Betty
Harms Collection.*

Kestner continued

Child doll, early shoulder head: Ca. 1880s. Perfect bisque head, plaster dome, good wig, set or sleep eyes; sometimes head is slightly turned; kid body with bisque lower arms; marked with size letters or numbers. (No mold numbers.)

Closed mouth:

15—17in (38—43cm)	$ 550—600*
20—22in (51—56cm)	700—800*
26in (66cm)	1000*

Open/closed mouth:

14—16in (36—41cm)	525—575

Bru-type body, swivel neck pouty, 20in (51cm) at auction **2300**
Bisque yoke and arms, swivel neck, 7in (18cm) at auction **2500**

Open mouth:

14—16in (36—41cm)	400—425
20—22in (51—56cm)	475—550
25in (64cm)	650—700

*Allow extra for a very pouty face or swivel neck.

12in (31cm) closed mouth shoulder head child "D." *Private Collection.*

Kestner continued

Child doll, bisque shoulder head, open mouth: Ca. 1892. Kid body, some with rivet joints. Plaster dome, good wig, sleep eyes, open mouth; dressed, all in good condition. (See *Kestner, King of Dollmakers* for photographs of mold numbers not pictured here.)

HEAD MARK: *154. 8 dep.*
D made in Germany

BODY MARK:

#154, 147, 148, 149, 166, 195:

12—13in (31—33cm)	**$275—300***
16—17in (41—43cm)	**375—400***
20—22in (51—56cm)	**450—500***
26—28in (66—71cm)	**700—800***

*Allow additional for a rivet jointed body.

28in (71cm) 147 Kestner shoulder head child. *H&J Foulke, Inc.*

16in (41cm) 195 Kestner shoulder head child with inset eyebrows. *H&J Foulke, Inc.*

Kestner continued

Child doll, open mouth: Bisque socket head on ball-jointed body; plaster dome, good wig, sleep eyes, open mouth; dressed; all in good condition. (See *Kestner, King of Dollmakers* for photographs of mold numbers not pictured here.)

HEAD MARK: D *made in Germany. 8. 162.*   **BODY MARK:** Excelsior DRP N. 70686 Germany

Early child, square cut teeth (no mold number):

10—11in (25—28cm)$	425—475
14—16in (36—41cm)	600—700

Mold numbers 129, 142, 144, 146, 152, 156, 160, 164, 167, 168, 171, 174, 196, 214:

12—14in (31—36cm)	400—450
16—17in (41—43cm)	425—450
19—22in (48—56cm)	475—550
24-26in (61-66cm)	600—700
28—30in (71—76cm)	800—900
33—36in (84—91cm)	1200—1600
42in (107cm)	2500

#133:

7in (18cm)	400

#155:

7—8in (18—20cm)	400—450

#171: Daisy, blonde mohair wig,

18in (46cm)	550—650

See color photograph on page 119.

24in (61cm) Kestner 164 child. *Private Collection.*

9½in (24cm) Kestner child with two **upper** square cut teeth. *Yvonne Baird Collection.*

Kestner continued

Character Child: 1909—on. Perfect bisque head character face, plaster pate, wig, painted or glass eyes, closed, open or open/closed mouth; good jointed composition body; dressed; all in good condition. (See *Kestner, King of Dollmakers* for photographs of mold numbers not pictured here.)

#143 (Pre 1987): (See photograph on page 119.)

7—8in (18—20cm)	$ 400—450
11—12in (28—31cm)	500—550
18—20in (46—51cm)	850—950

#178-190, 212:

Painted Eyes:

12in (31cm)	1800
15in (38cm)	2500
18in (46cm)	3200

Glass Eyes:

12in (31cm)	2300—2500
15in (38cm)	3000
18in (46cm)	3600—3800

#241:

18—22in (46—56cm)	3800—4500

#249:

20—22in (51—56cm)	1200—1400

#260:

8in (20cm) Toddler	425—450
12—14in (31—36cm) JCB or Toddler	700—750
18in (46cm) JCB or Toddler	800—900

#220, 239 Toddler:

20in (51cm)	3250—3500**
27in (69cm)	5500**

**Not enough price samples to compute a reliable range.

See page 8 for photograph of 183 character.

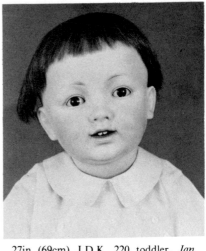

27in (69cm) J.D.K. 220 toddler. *Jan Foulke Collection.*

11in (28cm) 185 character child. *Yvonne Baird Collection.*

11in (28cm) 178 character child. *Yvonne Baird Collection.*

Kestner continued

Character Baby: 1910—on. Perfect bisque head, molded and/or painted hair or good wig, sleep or set eyes, open or open/closed mouth; bent-limb body; well dressed; nice condition. (See *Kestner, King of Dollmakers* for photographs of mold numbers not pictured here.)

MARK:

made in
F. Germany. 10
211
J.D.K.

#211, 226, JDK solid dome (See photograph on page 10.):

11—13in (28—33cm)	**$ 400—450**	
16—17in (41—43cm)	**575—675**	
20—22in (51—56cm)	**850—950**	
25in (64cm)	**1250—1400**	
18—19in (46—48cm) Toddler	**950—1000**	

#234, 235, 238 shoulder heads:

16—18in (41—46cm)	**650—700**

Hilda, #237, 245, solid dome:

11—13in (28—33cm)	**2000—2200**
16—17in (41—43cm)	**3000—3300**
20—22in (51—56cm)	**3800—4300**
24in (61cm)	**5000—5500**

#247:

12in (31cm)	**1000**
16in (41cm)	**1700**

#257, 262:

15—17in (38—43cm)	**600—700**
20—21in (51—53cm)	**850—950**
Toddler 27in (69cm)	**1550**

Solid dome, fat-cheeked:

15—17in (38—43cm)	**1000—1200**
23—24in (58—61cm)	**1700—1900**

All-bisque:

10in (25cm)	**650—750**
11½in (29cm)	**850—950**

Molded cap JDK:

17in (43cm) at auction	**9750**

(See photograph on page 9.)

20in (51cm) J.D.K. fat-cheeked character baby (no mold number). *Esther Schwartz Collection.*

Kestner continued

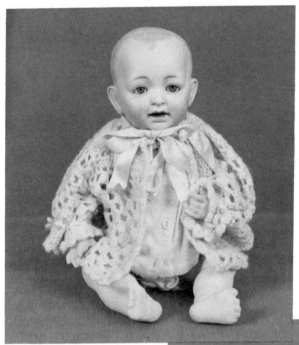

15in (38cm) J.D.K. character
baby (no mold number). *Leone
McMullen Collection.*

13in (33cm) J.D.K. 237 **Hilda**
character baby. *Yvonne Baird
Collection.*

Kestner continued

All-Bisque Child: Perfect all-bisque child jointed at shoulders and hips; mohair wig, sleeping eyes, open mouth with upper teeth; blue or pink painted stockings, black strap shoes. Naked or with appropriate clothes. Very good quality.

#150:

4—5in (10—13cm)	**$185—225**
7in (18cm)	**300—350**
8in (20cm)	**425—450**
9in (23cm)	**575—625**
11in (28cm)	**800—850**
12in (31cm)	**900—950**

7½in (19cm) Kestner 150 all-bisque child.
H&J Foulke, Inc.

Kestner continued

Gibson Girl: Ca. 1910. Perfect bisque shoulder head with good wig, glass eyes, closed mouth, up-lifted chin; kid body with bisque lower arms (cloth body with bisque lower limbs on small dolls); beautifully dressed; all in good condition; sometimes marked "Gibson Girl" on body.

#172:

10—12in (26—31cm) **$1200—1400**
20—21in (51—53cm) **3500—4000**

Lady Doll: Perfect bisque socket head, plaster dome, wig with lady hairdo, sleep eyes, open mouth with upper teeth; jointed composition body with molded breasts, nipped-in waist, slender arms and legs; appropriate lady clothes; all in good condition. (For photograph see *7th Blue Book*, page 248.)

MARK:

#162:

16—18in (41—46cm)**$1100—1400**

21in (53cm) 172 *Gibson Girl.* See color photograph on page 120. *Mary Lou Rubright Collection.*

Kestner continued

O.I.C. Baby: Perfect bisque solid dome head with screaming features, tiny glass eyes, wide open mouth with molded tongue; cloth body; dressed; all in good condition. Mold *#255*.

MARK: "255
3
O.I.C."

13in (33cm) **$1500—1600**

13in (33cm) O.I.C. Baby. *Dr. Carole Stoessel Zvonar Collection.*

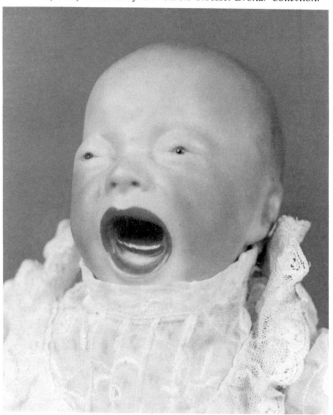

Siegfried: Perfect bisque solid dome head with molded hair and flange neck, sleep eyes, closed mouth, side nose, pronounced philtrum; cloth body with composition hands; dressed; all in good condition. Mold *#272*.

MARK:
Head circumference:

12—13in (31—33cm) **$1800—2000**

Siegfried
made in Germany
g

Kewpie

Maker: Various
Date: 1913—on
Size: 2in (5cm) up
Designer: Rose O'Neill, U.S.A. U.S. Agent: George Borgfeldt & Co., New York, N.Y., U.S.A.
Mark: Red and gold paper heart or shield on chest and round label on back

All-Bisque: Made by J. D. Kestner and other German firms. Often have imperfections in making. Sometimes signed on foot "O'Nei⌡⌠". Standing, legs together, arms jointed, blue wings, painted features, eyes to side.

Standing *Kewpie* with fireman's helmet. *Sandy Coons Collection.*

2—2½in (5—6cm)	$ 85—95
4—5in (10—13cm)	100—125
6in (15cm)	150
7in (18cm)	200—250
8—9in (20—23cm)	350—400
12—13in (31—33cm)	1200—1500
Jointed hips, 4in (10cm)	400—450
Shoulder head, 2½in (6cm)	200—250
Black Hottentot, 5in (13cm)	350
Button hole,	150—165
Pincushion, 2—3in (5—8cm)	200—250
Painted shoes and socks, 11in (28cm)	950

Group of all-bisque *Kewpies. Sandy Coons Collection.*

Kewpie continued

Action Kewpies (sometimes stamped: ©):

Thinker, 4in (10cm)	250—275
Kewpie with cat, 3½in (9cm)	350
Confederate Soldier, 3½in (9cm)	300
Kewpie holding pen, 3in (8cm)	350
Lying on stomach, 4in (10cm)	350—375
Gardener, Sweeper, Soldier, Farmer, 4in (10cm)	400
Kewpie with rabbit, 2in (5cm)	250—275
Doodledog:	
3in (9cm)	900
1½in (4cm)	450
Huggers, 3½in (9cm)	175
Guitar player, 3½in (9cm)	275
Traveler, 3½in (9cm)	275
Governor, 3½in (9cm)	350
Kewpie with teddy, 4in (10cm)	600
Kewpie with turkey, 2in (5cm)	350
Kewpie and *Doodledog* on beach, 3½in (9cm)	1500 up
Perfume bottle, 3½in (9cm)	450
Kewpie with rose, 2in (5cm)	250
Kewpie with umbrella and *Doodledog*, 3½in (9cm)	850
Kewpie with Prussian helmet, 6in (15cm)	550
Kewpie with drawstring bag, 4½in (12cm)	450
Kewpie in basket, 3in (8cm)	350

Kewpie with pen. *Sandy Coons Collection.*

Kewpie with cat. *Sandy Coons Collection.*

Kewpie continued

Bisque head on chubby jointed composition toddler body, glass eyes: Made by J. D. Kestner. (For photograph see *6th Blue Book*, page 247.)

MARK: "Ges. gesch.
O'Neill J.D.K."

10in (25cm) five-piece body	**$3000—3500****
12—14in (31—36cm)	**4000—4500****

**Not enough price samples to compute a reliable range.

Bisque head on cloth body:
12in (31cm) Glass eyes	**$2600—2800****
(Mold ***#1377*** made by Alt, Beck & Gottschalck)	**2500****
Painted eyes	**1600—2000****

**Not enough price samples to compute a reliable range.

12in (31cm) bisque head ***Kewpie*** on cloth body, mold #1377. *Yvonne Baird Collection.*

Kewpie continued

Celluloid: Made by Karl Standfuss, Deuben near Dresden, Saxony, Germany. Straight standing, arms jointed, blue wings; very good condition.

2½in (6cm)	$ 30—35
5in (13cm)	65
8in (20cm)	125
Black, 2½in (6cm)	60—65

All-Composition: Made by Cameo Doll Co., Rex Doll Co., and Mutual Doll Co., all of New York, N.Y., U.S.A. All-composition, jointed at shoulders, some at hips; good condition.

8in (20cm)	$110—125
11—13in (28—33cm)	150—175
Black, 12—13in (31—33cm)	225—275
Talcum container, 7in (18cm)	150—175

13in (33cm) composition *Kewpie*, all original with tag. *Maurine Popp Collection.*

Kewpie continued

All-Cloth: Made by Richard G. Kreuger, Inc., New York, N.Y., U.S.A. Patent number 1785800. Mask face with fat-shaped cloth body, including tiny wings and peak on head. Cloth label sewn in side seam.
10—12in (25—31cm) **$125—150**
18in (46cm) with tagged dress and bonnet **300**

Hard Plastic: Ca. 1950s.
Standing Kewpie, one piece with jointed arms, 8in (20cm) **$ 65—75**
Fully-jointed with sleep eyes; all original clothes, 13in (33cm) **300—350****

**Not enough price samples to compute a reliable range.

12in (31cm) ***Cuddle Kewpie****. H&J Foulke, Inc.*

13in (33cm) hard plastic ***Kewpie*** with sleep eyes, all original. *H&J Foulke, Inc.*

LEFT: 17in (43cm) Simon & Halbig 1248 black child. For further information see page 95. *Carol Green Collection.*

BELOW: 24in (61cm) Simon & Halbig 719 child with closed mouth. For further information see page 364. *Joanna Ott Collection.*

RIGHT: 7½in (19cm) Simon & Halbig all-bisque child, all original. For further information see page 365. *Private Collection.*

BELOW RIGHT: 24in (61cm) Simon & Halbig 1079 child. For further information see page 365. *Joanna Ott Collection.*

BELOW LEFT: 24in (61cm) Simon & Halbig 749 child with closed mouth. For further information see page 364. *Private Collection.*

16in (41cm) Simon & Halbig 1279 character child. For further information see page 367. *Private Collection.*

ABOVE: 20in (51cm) Steiff *Sailor*, all original. For further information see page 375. *Nancy Smith Collection.*

RIGHT: 23in (59cm) E. U. Steiner child. For further information see page 376. *H&J Foulke, Inc.*

LEFT: 11in (28cm) Steiff *Dutch Boy & Girl*, all original. For further information see page 375. *Nancy Smith Collection.*

17in (43cm) Jules Steiner A-9. For further information see page 379. *Private Collection.*

10in (25cm) **Tiny Terri Lee**, all original. For further information see page 381. *H&J Foulke, Inc.*

RIGHT: 22in (56cm) all-wood *Bébé Tout en Bois*. For further information see page 395. *H&J Foulke, Inc.*

BELOW: 14in (36cm) *Inge* by Wagner & Zetzsche. For further information see page 387. *Private Collection.*

RIGHT: 15in (38cm) Wislizenus toddler, mold **#110**. For further information see page 394. *H&J Foulke, Inc.*

BELOW: 11in (28cm) Northern Warlord, Royal Personage, Ca. 1840, all original. For further information see page 321. *Betty Lunz Collection.*

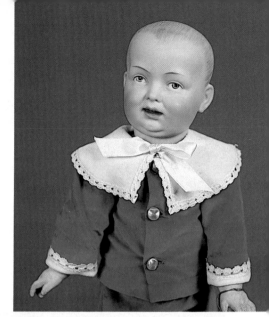

Kley & Hahn

Maker: Kley & Hahn, doll factory, Ohrdruf, Thüringia, Germany. Heads by Hertel, Schwab & Co. (100 series), Bähr & Pröschild (500 series) and J. D. Kestner (250, 680 and Walkure).

Date: 1902—on

Material: Bisque head, composition body

Trademarks: Walküre, Meine Einzige, Special, Dollar Princess

Mark:

> K&H <   K H
Germany   Walküre

Child Doll: Perfect bisque head, wig, glass eyes, open mouth; jointed composition child body; fully dressed; all in good condition.

#250 or *Walküre*

18—21in (46—53cm)	**$400—450**	
24—26in (61—66cm)	**550—600**	

Character Child: Perfect bisque head, wig, glass or painted eyes, closed mouth; jointed composition child or toddler body; fully dressed; all in good condition.

#520, 526, 536, 546, 549:

15—16in (36—38cm)	**$2700—2900**	
19—21in (48—53cm)	**3700—4300**	

#154, 166, closed mouth:

16—17in (41—43cm)	**2000—2200**

#154, 166, open mouth:

20in (51cm)

toddler	**1200—1300**

#169:

19—21in (48—53cm)

toddler	**3000—3500****

**Not enough price samples to compute a reliable range.

24in (61cm) Kley & Hahn Walküre. *Dolly Valk Collection.*

16in (41cm) Kley & Hahn 520 character child. *Betty Harms Collection.*

Kley & Hahn continued

Character Baby: Perfect bisque head with molded hair or good wig, sleep or painted eyes, open or closed mouth; bent-limb baby body; nicely dressed; all in good condition.

#138, 158, 160, 167, 176, 525, 531:

11—12in (28—31cm)	**$375—425***
16—18in (41—46cm)	**500—550***
23—24in (58—61cm)	**800—850***

#680, 568:

19—21in (48—53cm) toddler	**900—1000**

*Allow $100—150 extra for a toddler or jointed body.

15in (38cm) Kley & Hahn 525 character baby. *H&J Foulke, Inc.*

15in (38cm) Kley & Hahn 531 character. *Yvonne Baird Collection.*

Kling

Maker: Kling & Co., porcelain factory, Ohrdruf, Thüringia, Germany
Date: 1836—on (1870—on for dolls)
Material: Bisque or china shoulder head, cloth body, bisque lower limbs; bisque socket head, composition body, all-bisque
Mark: 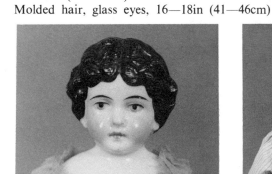 and numbers, such as *167, 176, 189, 190, 203, 372, 377*

China shoulder head: Ca. 1880. Black- or blonde-haired china head with bangs, sometimes with a pink tint; cloth body with china limbs or kid body; dressed; all in good condition.

#188, 189, 200 and others:

16—18in (41—46cm)	**$275—300**
20—22in (51—56cm)	**350—400**
25in (64cm)	**450**

Bisque shoulder head: Ca. 1880. Molded hair or mohair wig, painted eyes, closed mouth; cloth body with bisque lower limbs; dressed; in all good condition.

12—14in (31—36cm)	**$275—325**
18—20in (46—51cm)	**400—450**
23—25in (58—64cm)	**500—550**
Molded hair, glass eyes, 16—18in (41—46cm)	**500—600**

15in (38cm) 189 Kling china head with pink tint. *H&J Foulke, Inc.*

16in (41cm) Kling 140 bisque shoulder head. *H&J Foulke, Inc.*

Kling continued

Bisque head: Ca. 1890. Mohair or human hair wig, glass sleep eyes, open mouth; kid or cloth body with bisque lower arms or jointed composition body; dressed; all in good condition.

#373 or **377** shoulder head:

   13—15in (33—38cm) **$325—350**

   19—22in (48—56cm) **400—450**

#370 or **372** socket head:

   14—16in (36—41cm) **350—375**

   22—24in (56—61cm) **525—575**

All-bisque Child: Jointed shoulders and hips; wig, glass eyes, closed mouth; molded footwear. (For photograph see *7th Blue Book*, page 263.)

  MARK: Kling bell

             and/or

             "36-10n"

4in (10cm) **$185—195**

13in (33cm) Kling 377 shoulder head child made for Kämmer & Reinhardt, all original. *H&J Foulke, Inc.*

Knickerbocker

Maker: Knickerbocker Doll & Toy Co., New York, N.Y., U.S.A.
Date: 1937
Material: All-composition
Mark: (Embossed on dwarfs)
"WALT DISNEY
KNICKERBOCKER TOY CO."

Knickerbocker Seven Dwarfs: All-composition jointed at shoulders, stiff hips, molded shoes, individual character faces, painted features; mohair wigs or beards; jointed shoulders, molded and painted shoes; original velvet costumes and caps with identifying names: "Sneezy," "Dopey," "Grumpy," "Doc," "Happy," "Sleepy" and "Bashful."
12in (31cm)   **$150—165**

Knickerbocker Snow White: All-composition jointed at neck, shoulders and hips; black mohair wig with hair ribbon, brown lashed sleep eyes, open mouth; original clothing; all in good condition.
20in (51cm)   **$400—450**
With molded black hair and blue ribbon, 13in (33cm) **250—275**

12in (31cm) Knickerbocker *Happy*, all original. *H&J Foulke, Inc.*

Gebrüder Knoch

Maker: Gebrüder Knoch, porcelain factory, Neustadt, Thüringia, Germany
Date: 1887—on
Material: Bisque heads for kid, cloth or composition bodies
Mark:

G. K.
N.
Made in Germany
Ges. No. 216 Gesch.

Knoch Child Doll: Perfect bisque head, original or appropriate wig, sleep or
set eyes, open mouth; ball-jointed body; dressed; entire doll in good
condition.
12—14in (31—36cm) **$225—250**

Knoch Character Doll: Perfect bisque socket or shoulder head, molded hair,
painted eyes, open/closed mouth; composition, kid or cloth body; dressed;
entire doll in good condition.
#206, 216
16in (41cm)   **$ 450—550**
#246, molded cap, winking,
13in (33cm) at auction **1900**
#237, molded bonnet,
10in (25cm)   **350—400**

16in (41cm) Knoch character #216 shoulder head. *Lesley Hurford Collection.*

König & Wernicke

Maker: König & Wernicke, doll factory, Waltershausen, Thüringia, Germany.
Heads by Hertel, Schwab & Co. and Bähr & Pröschild
Date: 1912—on
Material: Bisque heads, composition bodies or all-composition
Trademarks: Meine Stolz, My Playmate
Mark: K 8 W
1070

Body Mark:

K & W Character: Bisque head with good wig, sleep eyes, open mouth; composition baby or toddler body; appropriate clothes; all in good condition.

#98, 99, 100, 1070:

14—16in (36—41cm)	**$475—525***
19—21in (48—53cm)	**650—750***
24—25in (61—64cm)	**850—950***

*Allow $50 extra for flirty eyes.
*Allow $100—150 extra for toddler body.

15in (38cm) 98 character baby made for K & W by H.S. & Co. *Private Collection.*

Richard G. Krueger, Inc.

Maker: Richard G. Krueger, Inc., New York, N.Y., U.S.A.
Date: 1917—on
Material: All-cloth, mask face
Mark: Cloth tag or label

All-Cloth Doll: Ca. 1930. Mask face with painted features, rosy cheeks, painted eyes with large black pupil and two highlights each eye, curly thick painted upper lashes, curly mohair wig on cloth cap; oil cloth body with hinged shoulders and hips. Simple dotted swiss dress with attached undie, pink taffeta coat and hat with lace trim. All in excellent condition.

LABEL: Krueger, N.Y.
              Reg. U.S. Pat Off.
              Made in U.S.A.

16in (41cm)	**$100—110**
20in (51cm)	**125—150**

20in (51cm) cloth doll of the type made by Krueger, all original. *H&J Foulke, Inc.*

Käthe Kruse

Maker: Käthe Kruse, Bad Kösen, Germany

Date: 1910—on

Material: Molded muslin head (hand-painted), jointed cloth body, later of hard plastic material.

Mark: On cloth: "Käthe Kruse" on sole of foot, sometimes also "Germany" and a number

Hard plastic on back: Turtle mark and "Käthe Kruse"

Käthe Kruse
81971

*Made in
Germany*

Cloth Käthe Kruse:Molded muslin head, hand-painted; jointed at shoulders and hips:

Doll I (1910—1929), painted hair, wide hips, 16—17in (41—43cm):

Mint, all original	**$1500—1800 up**
Good condition, suitably dressed	**850—950**

Doll IH (after 1929), wigged, 16—17in (41—43cm):

Mint, all original	**1200—1500**
Good condition, suitably dressed	**750—850**

Doll II (1922) "***Schlenkerchen***" Smiling Baby, 13in (33cm) **850—950**

Doll V & VI(1925) Babies "***Traumerchen***" (closed eyes) and "***Du Mein***"

(open eyes),
19½—23½in (50—60cm) **2200—2500**

Doll VII (1927)
14in (36cm) **900—1000**

Doll VIII (1929) wigged
"German Child" 20½in (52cm):

Mint, all original	**1200—1500**
Good condition, suitably dressed	**800—900**

Doll IX
(U.S. Zone Germany 1945—1951),
14in (36cm) **650—700**

See color photograph on page 187 of Doll I.

20½in (52cm) Käthe Kruse, Doll VIII, replaced clothing. *H&J Foulke, Inc.*

Käthe Kruse continued

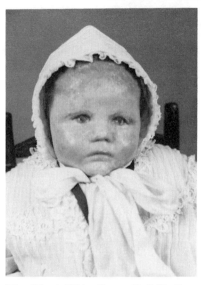

20in (51cm) Käthe Kruse, Doll V, Du Mein. *Betty Harms Collection.*

14in (36cm) Käthe Kruse, Doll IX, U.S. Zone Germany, all original. *H&J Foulke, Inc.*

All-Hard Plastic (Celluloid) Käthe Kruse: Wig or molded hair and sleep or painted eyes; jointed neck, shoulders and hips; original clothes; all in excellent condition. Turtle mark. (1955—1961).
16in (41cm)   **$325—375**

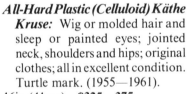

16in (41cm) hard plastic (celluloid) Käthe Kruse child, all original. *H&J Foulke, Inc.*

Käthe Kruse continued

Hard Plastic Head: Ca. 1950s—on. Hard plastic head with lovely wig, painted eyes; pink muslin body; original clothes; all in excellent condition.

U.S. Zone Germany
14in (36cm)   **$500—550**

Ca. 1952—1975:
10in (25cm)   **250—275**
14in (36cm)   **425—475**

1975—on:
10in (25cm)   **175—225**
14in (36cm)   **350—400**
18—20in (46—51cm)   **425—475**

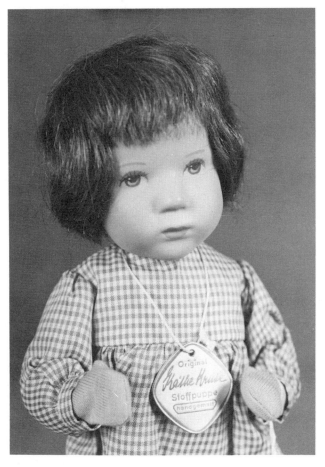

10in (25cm) Käthe Kruse *Linchen*, U.S. Zone Germany, all original. *H&J Foulke, Inc.*

Gebrüder Kuhnlenz

Maker: Gebrüder Kuhnlenz, porcelain factory, Kronach, Bavaria
Date: 1884—on
Material: Bisque head, composition or kid body
Size: Various
Mark: " G.K. "

G̲br̲ 165 K
9

and/or numbers, such as:
41-28   56-18   44-15   Germany

The first two digits are mold number; second two are size number.

GbrK

44-31

G. K. doll with closed mouth: Ca. 1890. Perfect bisque socket head, inset
glass eyes, closed mouth, round cheeks; jointed composition body; dressed;
all in good condition.
#32:

16—18in (41—46cm)	$1000—1200**
22—24in (56—61cm)	1500—1700**

#34, Bru-type, French JCB, Gosset label:

16—18in (41—46cm)	2500**

#38 shoulder head, kid body:

14—16in (36—41cm)	550—600**
22—23in (56—58cm)	800—900**

**Not enough price samples to compute a reliable range.

G. K. child doll: Ca. 1890—on.
Perfect bisque socket head with
distinctive face, almost a character look, long cheeks, sleep
eyes, open mouth, molded teeth;
jointed composition body, sometimes French; dressed; all in good
condition.

#41, 44, 56:

18—20in (46—51cm)	$ 650—750
24—26in (61—66cm)	850—950

#165:

14—16in (36—41cm)	325—350
22—24in (56—61cm)	425—475
34in (86cm)	1150

25in (64cm) G. K. Sunburst 44-31 child.
Betty Harms Collection.

Gebrüder Kuhnlenz continued

G. K. Tiny Dolls: Perfect bisque socket head, wig, stationary glass eyes, open mouth with molded teeth; five-piece composition body with molded shoes and socks; all in good condition. Usually mold ***#44***.

8—8½in (20—22cm)	**$150—175**
Closed mouth, Belton-type head, 8in (20cm)	**550—600**

7in (18cm) 44-15 child, all original. *H&J Foulke, Inc.*

Lanternier

Maker: A Lanternier & Cie. porcelain factory of Limoges, France
Date: 1915—1924
Material: Bisque head, papier-mâché body
Mark:

```
FABRICATION
FRANÇAISE
```

AL ε Cⁱᵉ
LIMOGES
A   1

Marked Lanternier Child: Ca. 1915. Perfect bisque head, good or original wig, large stationary eyes, open mouth, pierced ears; papier-mâché jointed body; pretty clothes; all in good condition.

Cherie, Favorite or ***La Georgienne***
16—18in (41—46cm) **$ 650—750**
22—24in (56—61cm)   **850—950***
28in (71cm)   **1300—1400***

*Allow extra for lovely face and bisque.

18in (46cm) Lanternier child. *Doodlebug Doll & Toy Shop.*

Lanternier continued

Lanternier Lady: Ca. 1915. Perfect bisque head with adult look, good wig, stationary glass eyes, open/closed mouth with molded teeth; composition lady body; dressed; all in good condition. (For photograph see *7th Blue Book*, page 271.)

Lorraine
16—18in (41—46cm)   **$850—1250***

*Depending upon costume and quality.

Marked Toto: Ca. 1915. Perfect bisque smiling character face, good wig, glass eyes, open/closed mouth with molded teeth, pierced ears; jointed French composition body; dressed; all in good condition.
17—19in (43—48cm)   **$900—1000**

19½in (50cm) unmarked ***Toto*** character child. *Esther Schwartz Collection.*

Lenci

Maker: Enrico & Elenadi Scavini, Turin, Italy
Date: 1920—on
Material: Pressed felt head with painted features, jointed felt bodies
Size: 5—45in (13—114cm)
Mark: "LENCI" on cloth and various paper tags; sometimes stamped on bottom of foot

Lenci: All-felt (sometimes cloth torso) with swivel head, jointed shoulders and hips; painted features, eyes usually side-glancing; original clothes, often of felt or organdy; in excellent condition.

Miniatures and Mascottes:

8—9in (20—23cm) Regionals	$ 225—275
Children or unusual costumes	300—400
Children #300, 109, 149, 159, 111:	
13in (33cm)	750 up
16—18in (41—46cm)	950 up
20—22in (51—56cm)	1250 up
"Lucia" face, 14in (36cm)	500 up
Ladies and long-limbed novelty dolls, 24—28in (61—71cm)	1600 up
Glass eyes, 20in (51cm)	2800—3000
Celluloid-type, 6in (15cm)	40—50
"Surprised Eye" (round painted eyes) 20in (51cm)	1800 up
#1500, scowling face, 17—19in (43—48cm)	1500—1800
Baby, 14—18in (36—46cm)	1800 up
Indian girl with papoose, 18in (46cm) at auction	2700
Baby, composition head, 14in (36cm) at auction	1000

Collector's Note: Mint examples of rare dolls will bring higher prices. To bring the prices quoted, Lenci dolls must be clean and have good color. Faded and dirty dolls bring only about one-third to one-half these prices.

Lenci continued

24in (61cm) Lenci girl, all original. *Beth Foulke Collection.*

7½in (19cm) Lenci sailor character, all original. *Esther Schwartz Collection.*

25in (64cm) Lenci in cowgirl outfit, all original. *Esther Schwartz Collection.*

Lenci-Type

Maker: Various Italian, French and English firms such as Marguerin, Alma
and others.
Date: 1920—1940
Material: Felt and cloth
Size: 6in (15cm) up
Mark: Various paper labels, if any

Felt or Cloth Doll: Mohair wig, painted features; original clothes or costume.
Child dolls, 16—18in (41—46cm) up to **$650** depending upon quality
Foreign costume,

    7½—8½in (19—22cm)   **$35—40**
    12in (31cm)   **75—85**

13in (33cm) Consuelo Originals (Italy),
all original. *H&J Foulke, Inc.*

Limbach.

Maker: Limbach Porzellanfabrik, Limbach, Thüringia,
Germany (porcelain factory)
Date: Factory started in 1772
Material: Bisque head, composition body; all bisque
Mark:

MADE IN GERMANY

All-Bisque Child: Ca. 1900. Child all of bisque (sometimes pink bisque) with
wire jointed shoulders and hips; molded hair (often with a blue molded bow)
or bald head with mohair wig, painted eyes, closed mouth, white stockings,
blue garters, brown slippers or strap shoes.

MARK: P23

GERMANY

4—5in (10—13cm) $ 75—85
Glass eyes,
5in (13cm) **150—165**
Character, jointed arms only,
4—5in (10—13cm) 75—85

All-Bisque Baby: Ca. 1910. Baby
with painted hair and facial features; wire jointed shoulders and
hips, bent arms and legs; bare
feet.
MARK: Clover and number
with P.
4—5in (10—13cm) **$ 75—95**
11—12in (28—31cm) **500**

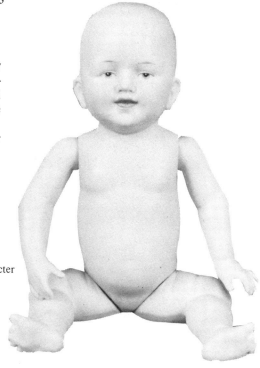

11½in (29cm) Limbach 8660 character
baby, fine quality. *H&J Foulke, Inc.*

Limbach continued

Limbach Child Doll: 1893—1899; 1919—on. Perfect bisque head, good wig, glass eyes, open-mouth with teeth; composition jointed body; dressed; all in good condition. ***Wally, Rita*** or ***Norma*** after 1919.

17—19in (43—48cm) **$450—500****
23—24in (58—61cm)   **600—650****

**Not enough price samples to compute a reliable range.

19in (48cm) child with incised clover. *Joanna Ott Collection.*

Albert Marque

Maker: Unknown, possibly artist produced
Date: 1916
Material: Bisque head, jointed composition body with bisque lower arms
Size: 22in (56cm) one size only
Designer: Albert Marque, French sculptor
Mark: a $\mathcal{M}$ arque

A. Marque Doll: Bisque head with wistful character face, mohair wig, paperweight eyes, closed mouth; jointed composition body of special design with bisque lower arms and hands, fixed wrists; appropriate clothes (some original ones from Paris designer Margaines-Lacroix).
22in (56cm) at auction **$43,000**

22in (56cm) Signed "A. Marque." *Courtesy of Richard W. Withington, Inc.*

Armand Marseille
(A.M.)

Maker: Armand Marseille of Köppelsdorf, Thüringia, Germany (porcelain and doll factory)

Date: 1885—on

Material: Bisque socket and shoulder head, composition, cloth or kid body

Mark:

Armand Marseille
Germany
990
A 9/0 M

Child Doll: 1890—on. Perfect bisque head, nice wig, set or sleep eyes, open mouth; composition ball-jointed body or jointed kid body with bisque lower arms; pretty clothes; all in good condition.

#390, (larger sizes marked only "A. [size] M."), *Florodora* (composition body):

12—14in (31—36cm)	$ 200—250
17—19in (43—48cm)	300—350
23—24in (58—61cm)	400—450
28—30in (71—76cm)	550—650
35—36in (89—91cm)	1100—1200
40—42in (102—107cm)	1800—2000
Five-piece composition body, 6—9in (15—23cm)	135—165
Closed mouth, 5—5½in (12—14cm)	200—225

#1894 (composition body):

14—16in (36—41cm)	375—425
21—23in (53—58cm)	550—600

#370, 3200, 1894 Florodora and other shoulder heads:

11—12in (28—31cm)	150
14—16in (36—41cm)	185—225
22—24in (56—61cm)	325—375

See color photograph on page 189.

Queen Louise:

12in (31cm)	300
23—25in (58—64cm)	450—500

Baby Betty:

14—16in (36—41cm)	350—400

#2000:

16in (41cm)	500**

**Not enough price samples to compute a reliable range.

Armand Marseille (A.M.) continued

24in (61cm) A.M. 390, all original. *H&J Foulke, Inc.*

23in (58cm) A.M. 1894, all original. *H&J Foulke, Inc.*

Name shoulder head child: 1898 to World War I. Perfect bisque shoulder head marked with doll's name, jointed kid or cloth body, bisque lower arms; good wig, glass eyes, open mouth; well dressed; all in good condition. Names include ***Rosebud, Lilly, Alma, Mabel, Darling, Beauty*** and ***Princess.***

12—14in (31—36cm)	**$150—185**
20—22in (51—56cm)	**300—350**
25in (64cm)	**375—400**

25in (64cm) ***Alma*** shoulder head. *H&J Foulke, Inc.*

Armand Marseille (A.M.) continued

Character Children: 1910—on.
Perfect bisque head, molded hair
or wig, glass or painted eyes,
open or closed mouth; composition body; dressed; all in good
condition.

#230 Fany (molded hair):
15—16in (38—41cm)	**$4500—5500**
19in (48cm)	**7500—8500**

#231 Fany (wigged):
12—13in (31—33cm)	**3200—3500**
16—17in (41—43cm)	**4500—5200**

#250:
15—16in (38—41cm)	**800—850****

#400 (child body):
14—15in (36—38cm)	**2500—3000**

#500, 600:
15in (38cm)	**450—550**

#550 (painted eyes):
11—13in (28—33cm)	**1200—1700****

#550 (glass eyes):
18—20in (46—51cm)	**3000**

A.M. (intaglio eyes):
16—17in (41—43cm)	**3500 up**

**Not enough price samples to
compute a reliable range.

See color photographs on pages 188 and 189.

ABOVE RIGHT: 10in (25cm) A.M. 550
with painted eyes. *Private Collection.*

14in (36cm) A.M. 400, child body. *Esther
Schwartz Collection.*

Armand Marseille (A.M.) continued

Character Baby: 1910—on. Perfect bisque head, good wig, sleep eyes, open mouth some with teeth; composition bent-limb body; suitably dressed; all in nice condition.

Mold #990, 985, 971, 996, 1330, 326 (solid dome), 980, 991, 327, 329 and others:

13—15in (33—38cm)$	350—400
18—20in (46—51cm)	475—525
23—24in (58—61cm)	675—750

#233:

13—15in (33—38cm)	425—475
20in (51cm)	600—650

#251/248 (open/closed mouth):

12—15in (31—38cm)	1250—1500

#251/248 (open mouth):

12—15in (31—38cm)	650—850

#410 (2 rows teeth):

15—16in (38—41cm)	900—1000

#518:

16—18in (41—46cm)	500—600

#560A:

15—17in (38—43cm)	500—550

#580, 590 (open/closed mouth):

14—15in (31—38cm)	1000—1100
18—20in (46—51cm)	1400—1600

#590 (open mouth):

16—18in (41—46cm)	850—950

Kiddiejoy (shoulder head, mama body):

19in (48cm)	475

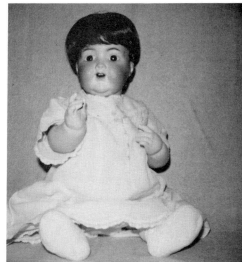

ABOVE RIGHT: 11in (28cm) 233 character baby. *H&J Foulke, Inc.*

A.M. 991 character baby. *Courtesy of Hazel Scherf.*

Armand Marseille (A.M.) continued

Infant: 1924—on. Solid-dome bisque head with molded and/or painted hair, sleep eyes; composition body or hard-stuffed jointed cloth body or soft-stuffed cloth body; dressed; all in good condition.

#351, 341 Kiddiejoy and Our Pet:
Head circumference:

10in (25cm)	**$275**
12—13in (31—33cm)	**350—425**
15in (38cm)	**600—650**
Painted bisque, 10in (25cm)	**150**

#352:

17—20in (43—51cm) long	**500—600**

#347:
Head circumference:

12—13in (31—33cm)	**450—500**

OPPOSITE PAGE: 24in (61cm) A.M. 980 character baby. *Dr. Carole Stoessel Zvonar Collection.*

RIGHT: 20in (51cm) A.M. 352 baby. *Dr. Carole Stoessel Zvonar Collection.*

9½in (24cm) h.c. A.M. 341 infant. *H&J Foulke, Inc.*

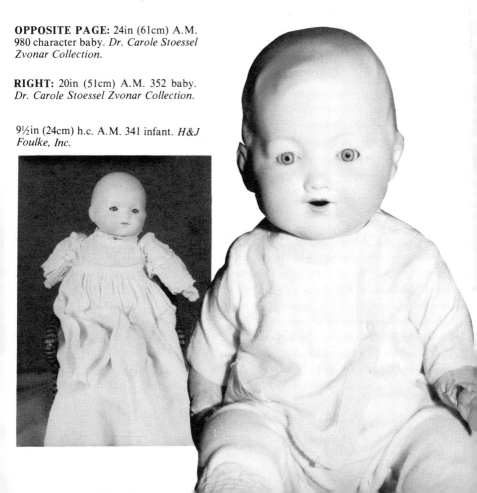

Armand Marseille (A.M.) continued

Marked Just Me Character: Ca. 1925. Perfect bisque socket head, curly wig, glass eyes to side, closed mouth; composition body; dressed; all in good condition. (For photograph see *7th Blue Book*, page 285.) Some of these dolls, particularly the painted bisque ones, were used by Vogue Doll Company in the 1930s and will be found with original Vogue labeled clothes.

MARK:

Just ME
Registered
Germany
A 310/5/0 M

9in (23cm)	**$1000—1100**
11in (28cm)	**1200—1400**
Painted bisque: 7—8in (18—20cm)	**500—600**

Lady: 1910—1930. Bisque head with mature face, mohair wig, sleep eyes, open or closed mouth; composition lady body with molded bust, long slender arms and legs; appropriate clothes; all in good condition. (For photograph see *6th Blue Book*, page 271.)

#401 and **400** (slim body):

14in (36cm)	
Open mouth	**$ 750—850**
Closed mouth	**1300—1500**
Painted bisque, closed mouth	**725—775**

#300 (H.A.):

9in (23cm)	**800—900****

**Not enough price samples to compute a reliable range.

Marked Baby Phyllis: Baby Phyllis Doll Co., Brooklyn, N.Y., U.S.A. Heads by Armand Marseille. Perfect solid dome bisque head with painted hair, sleep eyes, closed mouth; cloth body with composition hands; appropriate clothes; all in good condition. (For photograph see *5th Blue Book*, page 57.)

MARK:

BABY PHYLLIS
Made in Germany
2 4014

Head circumference: 12—13in (31—33cm)   **$400—450**

Marked Baby Gloria: Perfect solid dome head with molded and painted hair, sleep eyes, smiling face with open mouth and two upper teeth, dimples; cloth mama doll body with composition limbs; appropriately dressed; all in good condition. (For photograph see *5th Blue Book*, page 56.)

MARK:

Baby Gloria
Germany

15—16in (38—41cm) long   **$550—650**

Mascotte

Maker: May Freres Cie, 1890—1897; Jules Nicholas Steiner, 1898—on. Paris, France

Date: 1890—1902

Material: Bisque head, composition and wood jointed body

Mark:

"BÉBÉ MASCOTTE
PARIS"

Bébé Mascotte: Bisque socket head, good wig, closed mouth, paperweight eyes, pierced ears; jointed composition and wood body; appropriate clothes; all in good condition.

20—24in (51—61cm)	**$3800—4500**
30—31in (76—79cm)	**6000—7000**

See color photograph on page 190.

Mattel — Barbie®

Maker: Mattel, Inc., Hawthorne, C.A., U.S.A.

Date: 1959 to present

Material: Hard plastic and vinyl

Size: 11½—12in (29—31cm)

Mark: 1959—1962: Barbie TM/Pats. Pend./© MCMLVIII/by/Mattel, Inc.
1963—1968: Midge TM/© 1962/Barbie®/© 1958/by/Mattel, Inc.
1964—1966: © 1958/Mattel, Inc./U.S. Patented/U.S. Pat. Pend.
1966—1969: © 1966/Mattel, Inc./U.S. Patented/U.S. Pat. Pend./
Made in Japan

First Barbie®: 1959. Vinyl; white irises, pointed eyebrows, ponytail, black and white striped bathing suit, holes in feet to fit stand, gold hoop earrings; mint condition.

11½in (29cm) boxed	**$1500**
Doll only, no box or accessories	
Mint	**1200**
Very good	**800**
Stand	**100—150**
Shoes	**15**

Second Barbie: 1959—1960. Vinyl; same as above, but no holes in feet, some wore pearl earrings; mint condition. Made 3 months only.

11½in (29cm) boxed	**$1500**
Doll only, no box or accessories, very good	**800**

Third Barbie: 1960. Vinyl; same as above, but with blue irises and curved eyebrows; no holes in feet; mint condition.

11½in (29cm) boxed	**$350**
Doll only	**150**

Fourth Barbie: 1960. Vinyl; same as #3 but of flesh-toned vinyl; mint condition.

11½in (29cm) boxed	**$350**
Doll only	**150**

Sleep-Eyed Miss Barbie®: 1964, bendable knees.

11½in (29cm) boxed with accessories, mint	**$350**
Doll with accessories, no box	**150**

Other Dolls:

Black Francie®, 1967, mint in package	$500
Ken® **#1**, mint in box	75—80
Ken, bendable knees, mint in box	100
Side-Part Barbie®, bendable knees, mint in box	450—500
Hair Happenin's Barbie®, 1971, mint in box	500
Hair Happenin's Francie®, 1970, mint in box	85
Truly Scrumptious®, 1969, mint in box	375
mint, no box	200
Supersize Barbie®, bride, mint in box	85
swimsuit, mint in box	55
Twiggy®, 1967, mint in box	100
Midge®, bendable knee, mint in box	125
Bubble Cut Barbie®, 1963—on, mint in box	75—100
Gift Sets	350—500 up
Allen®, bendable knee, mint in box	100

Most other dolls are in the $15—35 price
range except for a few harder to find
models.

Outfits:

Roman Holiday, mint in package	$250
Gay Parisienne, mint in package	250
Easter Parade, mint in package	250
Brown mink coat, mint in package	800 up
Not in package	500 up
Barbie Baby Sits®, mint in package	100
Dogs & Duds®, mint in package	85
Dog only	35

#1 **Barbie**, mint and all original. *Glenn Mandeville Colletion.*

Mattel - Barbie continued

Close-up of #1 **Barbie** to show pointed eyebrow and white iris. *Glenn Mandeville Collection.*

Truly Scrumptious, all original but missing hat. *Claire Kline Collection.*

Ken with molded blonde hair, 1964. *Claire Kline Collection.*

Mengersgereuth

Maker: Porzellanfabrik Mengersgereuth, porcelain factory, Mengersgereuth, Sonneberg, Thüringia, Germany

Date: 1908—on

Material: Bisque head, composition or kid body

Mark:

PM
914.
Germany
1

Herzi
Germany
7

Marked Child: Perfect bisque head, wig, sleep eyes, open mouth; kid body with bisque hands or composition body; appropriate clothing; all in good condition.

Shoulder head with triangle mark, 24—26in (61—66cm)   **$550—650****

Trebor, composition body, 16—18in (41—46cm)   **425—475****

**Not enough price samples to compute a reliable range.

Marked Character Baby: Ca. 1910—on. Perfect bisque socket head, good wig, sleep eyes, open mouth; five-piece composition bent-limb baby body; dressed; all in good condition. Molds **914, 23, Grete** or **_Herzi_**.

12—14in (31—36cm)	**$325—375**
18—20in (46—51cm)	**475—525**
23—24in (58—61cm)	**700—750**

4½in (12cm) 151 shoulder head with triangle mark. _H&J Foulke, Inc._

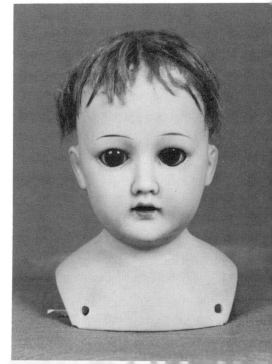

Metal Heads

Maker: Buschow & Beck, Germany (Minerva); Karl Standfuss, Germany
(Juno); Alfred Heller, Germany (Diana)
Date: Ca. 1888—on
Material: Metal shoulder head, kid or cloth body
Mark:

Marked Metal Head: Metal shoulder head on cloth or kid body, bisque or
composition hands; dressed; very good condition, not repainted.

With molded hair, painted eyes, 12—14in (31—36cm)	**$110—135**
With molded hair, glass eyes, 12—14in (31—36cm)	**150—175**
18—20in (46—51cm)	**200—225**
With wig and glass eyes, 14—16in (36—41cm)	**225—250**
20—22in (51—56cm)	**275—325**

21in (53cm) metal head with glass eyes. *H&J Foulke Inc.*

Missionary Ragbabies

Maker: Julia Beecher, Elmira, N.Y., U.S.A.
Date: 1893—1910
Material: All-cloth
Size: 16—23in (41—58cm)
Designer: Julia Jones Beecher
Mark: None

Beecher Baby: Handmade stuffed stockinette doll with looped wool hair, painted eyes and mouth, needle-sculpted face; appropriately dressed; all in good condition.

20—23in (51—59cm)	**$2500 up****
Fair condition, 18in (46cm)	**1600**

**Not enough price samples to compute a reliable range.

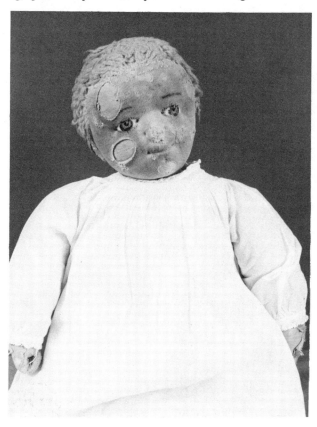

23in (58cm) Beecher ***Missionary Ragbaby.***

Molly-'es

Maker: International Doll Co., Philadelphia, PA, U.S.A. Made clothing only. Purchased undressed dolls from various manufacturers.
Date: 1920s—on
Material: All-cloth or all-composition, later hard plastic and vinyl
Clothes Designer: Mollye Goldman
Mark: Usually a cardboard tag, dolls unmarked except for vinyl

---

Molly-'es Composition Dolls: All-composition, jointed at neck, shoulders and hips; molded hair or wigs, sleep eyes; beautiful original outfits; all in good condition. (For photographs see *7th Blue Book*, page 291 and *6th Blue Book*, page 278.)

Babies, 12—15in (31—38cm)	**$125—150**
Toddlers, 14—16in (36—41cm)	**150—175**
Ladies, 18—21in (46—53cm)	**350**
Sabu, 15in (38cm)	**425—450**

Internationals: All-cloth with mask faces, mohair wigs (sometimes yarn), painted features; variety of costumes, all original clothes; in excellent condition with wrist tag.

13in (33cm)   **$65—75**

13in (33cm) *Molly-'es Scots girl*, all original. *H&J Foulke, Inc.*

Mothereau

Maker: Alexandre Mothereau, Paris, France
Date: 1880—1895
Material: Bisque head, wood and composition body
Trademark: Bébé Mothereau
Mark: B.M.

Bébé Mothereau: Perfect bisque head, beautiful blown glass eyes, closed
mouth, good wig, pierced ears; wood and composition jointed body;
beautifully dressed; all in good condition.
26—28in (66—71cm)   **$20,000**

27½in (70cm) B 11 M Child. *Wayne and Kay Jensen Collection.*

Munich Art Dolls

Maker: Marion Kaulitz
Date: 1908—1912
Material: All-composition, fully-jointed bodies
Size: Various
Designer: Paul Vogelsanger, and others
Mark: Sometimes signed on doll's neck

Munich Art Dolls: Molded composition character heads with hand-painted
   features; fully-jointed composition bodies; dressed; all in good condition.
   18—19in (46—48cm)   **$2500—3000****

**Not enough price samples to compute a reliable range.

18in (46cm) Munich Art Doll. See color photograph on page 186. *Yvonne Baird Collection.*

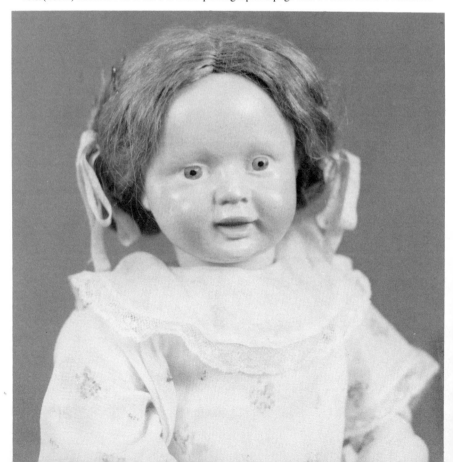

Nancy Ann

Maker: Nancy Ann Storybook Dolls Co., South San Francisco, CA., U.S.A.
Date: Mid 1930s
Material: Painted bisque, later plastic
Mark: Painted Bisque: Hard Plastic:

"Story	"STORYBOOK
Book	DOLLS
Doll	U.S.A.
U.S.A."	TRADEMARK
	REG."

Also a wrist tag identifying particular model

Marked Storybook Doll: Painted bisque, mohair wig, painted eyes; one-piece body, head and legs, jointed arms; original clothes; excellent condition.

Painted Bisque	**$ 45 up**
Jointed legs,	**60 up**
Swivel neck,	**60 up**
Hard Plastic	**40 up**
Bent-limb baby:	
Painted bisque	**80—90**
Hard plastic	**65—75**
Nancy Ann Style Show, hard plastic, 17in (43cm)	**400 up**
Muffie, hard plastic, 8in (20cm)	**100 up**

Painted bisque ***Lucy Locket***, all original. *H&J Foulke, Inc.*

4in (10cm) hard plastic boy and girl, all original. *H&J Foulke, Inc.*

Ohlhaver

Maker: Gebrüder Ohlhaver, doll factory, Sonneberg, Thüringia, Germany. Heads made by Gebrüder Heubach, Ernst Heubach and Porzellanfabrik Mengersgereuth.

Date: 1912—on

Material: Bisque socket head, ball-jointed composition body

Trademarks: Revalo

Mark:

Revalo
Germany
3

Revalo Character Baby or Toddler: Perfect bisque socket head, good wig, sleep eyes, hair eyelashes, painted lower eyelashes, open mouth; ball-jointed toddler or baby bent-limb body; dressed; all in good condition. (For photograph see *7th Blue Book*, page 296.)

#22: 16—18in (41—46cm)   **$550—650***

*Allow $150 extra for toddler body.

12in (31cm) character girl with molded hair band. *Private Collection.*

Revalo Character Doll: Bisque head with molded hair, painted eyes, open/closed mouth; composition body; dressed; all in good condition.

Coquette,
  10—12in (25—31cm)**$600—650**

Revalo Child Doll: Bisque socket head, good wig, sleep eyes, hair eyelashes, painted lower eyelashes, open mouth; ball-jointed composition body; dressed; all in good condition. Sometimes marked only *150*. (For photograph see *7th Blue Book*, page 296.)

15—17in (38—43cm)   **$450—500**
21—23in (53—58cm)   **600—650**

Oriental Dolls

Japanese Traditional Children: 1850—on. Papier-mâché swivel head on shoulder plate, hips, lower legs and feet (early ones have jointed wrists and ankles); cloth midsection, cloth (floating) upper arms and legs; hair wig, dark glass eyes, pierced ears and nostrils; original or appropriate clothes; all in good condition.

12—14in (31—36cm)	**$250—300**
18—20in (46—51cm)	**400—500**
Boy, 18—20in (46—51cm)	**450—550**
Ca. 1920s, 13—15in (33—38cm)	**110—135**
17—18in (43—46cm)	**175—200**
Ca. 1940s, 12—14in (31—36cm)	**80—90**
Traditional Lady, 1920s,	
10—12in (25—31cm)	**150**
1940s, 12—14in (31—36cm)	**85—95**
Traditional Warrior, 1920s,	
11—12in (28—31cm)	**200 up**
Royal Personnages, 1920s & 1930s,	
7—8in (18—20cm)	**100—125**
12in (31cm)	**200 up**

See color photographs on pages 115 and 193.

Japanese Traditional Baby Doll:
Ca. 1920—on. Papier-mâché with bent arms and legs; hair wig, dark glass eyes; original or appropriate clothes; all in good condition. (For photograph see *6th Blue Book*, page 180.)

7—8in (18—20cm)	**$ 60—65**
11—12in (28—31cm)	**90—110**
18in (46cm)	**175—225**

Japanese Baby with Bisque Head:
Ca. 1926—on. White bisque head, sleep eyes, closed mouth; five-piece papier-mâché body; original clothes; excellent condition.

7—8in (18—20cm)	**$ 45—55**
11—12in (28—31cm)	**125—150**
18in (46cm)	**275—300**

6in (15cm) Japanese baby with bisque head. *H&J Foulke, Inc.*

Oriental Dolls continued

Oriental Bisque Dolls: Ca. 1900—on. Made by German firms such as Simon & Halbig, Armand Marseille, J. D. Kestner and others. Bisque head tinted yellow; matching ball-jointed or baby body.

S&H 1329 girl,
13—14in (33—36cm)	**$1700—2000**
18—19in (46—48cm)	**2400—2600**
A.M. 353 baby, 10—12in (25—31cm)	**800—1000**
18—20in (46—51cm)	**1700—1900**
J.D.K. 243 baby, 13—15in (33—38cm)	**4500 up**
S&H 1099, 1129, and 1199 girl, 14—16in (36—41cm)	**2400—2600**
#220, 16—17in (41—43cm)	**3000—3400**
A.M. girl, 8—9in (20—23cm)	**600—700**
#164, 16—17in (41—43cm)	**2200—2400**
JDK molded hair baby, 17in (43cm)	**5000 up****
All-bisque S&H, 5½in (14cm)	**550**
French, bare feet, 5in (13cm)	**875****
BSW #500, 14—15in (36—38cm)	**1800—2000**
Unmarked, 4½in (12cm) painted eyes	**150—175**
Painted bisque,	
A.M. 353, 13in (33cm)	**500**

**Not enough price samples to compute a reliable average.

See color photographs on pages 185 and 190.

20in (51cm) S&H 1329 Oriental. *Private Collection.*

15¾in (39cm) Kestner Oriental baby with molded hair, incised " ⅃ ." *Private Collection.*

Oriental Dolls continued

13in (33cm) A.M. 353 Oriental toddler with painted bisque head, all original. *H&J Foulke, Inc.*

12in (31cm) *Ming Ming* baby, all original. *H&J Foulke, Inc.*

Baby Butterfly: 1911—1913. Made by E. I. Horsman. Composition head and hands, cloth body; painted black hair, painted features. (For photograph see *6th Blue Book*, page 286.)

13in (33cm) **$175****

**Not enough price samples to compute a reliable average.

Ming Ming Baby: Quan-Quan Co., Los Angeles and San Francisco, CA., U.S.A. Ca. 1930. All-composition baby, jointed at shoulders and hips; painted facial features; sometimes with black yarn hair, original costume of colorful taffeta with braid trim; feet painted black or white for shoes.

10—12in (25—31cm) **$100—125**

Papier-mâché
(So-Called French-Type)

Maker: Heads by German firms such as Johann Müller of Sonneberg and
Andreas Voit of Hildburghausen, were sold to French and other doll
makers

Date: 1816—1860

Material: Papier-mâché shoulder head, pink kid body

Mark: None

French-type Papier-mâché: Shoulder head with painted black pate, brush
marks around face, nailed on wig (often missing), set-in glass eyes, closed or
open mouth with bamboo teeth, pierced nose; pink kid body with stiff arms
and legs; appropriate old clothes; all in good condition, showing some wear.

18—20in (46—51cm)	**$1400—1600**
24—26in (61—66cm)	**2000—2200**
Painted eyes, 12in (31cm)	**750—800**

28in (71cm) so-called French-type papier-mâché. See color photograph on page 191.
Private Collection.

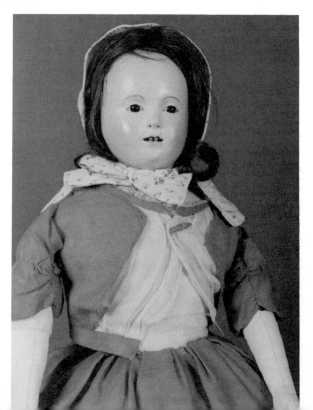

Papier-mâché
(German)

Maker: Various German firms of Sonneberg such as Johann Müller, Müller & Strasburger, F. M. Schilling, Heinrich Steir, A. Wislizenus, and Cuno & Otto Dressel

Date: 1816—on

Material: Papier-mâché shoulder head, cloth body, sometimes leather arms or kid body with wood limbs

---

Papier-mâché Shoulder Head: Ca. 1820s to 1850s. Unretouched shoulder head, molded hair, painted eyes; cloth body; original or appropriate old clothing; entire doll in fair condition. (For photograph see *6th Blue Book*, page 291.)

22—24in (56—61cm)	**$ 800—1000**
Glass eyes: 24in (61cm)	**1200—1400**

Molded Hair Papier-mâché: (so-called Milliners' models.) 1820s-1860s. Unretouched shoulder head, various molded hairdos, eyes blue, black or brown, painted features; original kid body, wooden arms and legs; original or very old handmade clothing; entire doll in fair condition.

7—8in (18—20cm)	**$ 300—350 up***
11—13in (28—33cm)	**500 up***
16—17in (41—43cm)	**650 up***
21—22in (53—56cm)	**800 up***
Partially molded hair with real curls framing face, 14in (36cm)	**1600**
Side curls with braided bun, 19in (48cm)	**1800**
Long curls with fancy bun, 21in (53cm)	**1700**
Side curls with high beehive, 23in (58cm)	**2500**

*Depending upon rarity and desirability of hairdo.

7in (18cm) molded hair papier-mâché doll, all original. *H&J Foulke, Inc.*

Papier-Mâché (German) continued

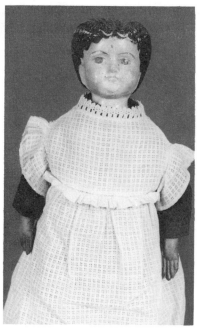

16in (41cm) molded hair papier-mâché lady, all original. *Joanna Ott Collection.*

19in (48cm) Sonneberg-type papier-mâché doll. *H&J Foulke, Inc.*

Sonneberg-type Papier-mâché: Ca. 1880—1910. Shoulder head with molded and painted black or blonde hair, painted eyes, closed mouth; cloth body sometimes with leather arms; old or appropriate clothes; all in good condition, showing some wear.

MARK: Usually unmarked. Some marked.

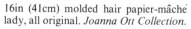

14—16in (36—41cm)	$225—275
19—21in (48—53cm)	325—375
24—25in (61—64cm)	450—500
Glass eyes, 23in (58cm)	550

A.W.
Serial3

or

M & S
Superior
2015

See color photograph on page 193.

Patent Washable-type: 1880s to 1914.

See page 142.

Papier-Mâché (German) continued

25in (64cm) Patent Washable-type papier-mâché child. *H&J Foulke, Inc.*

13in (33cm) *Gura* all-composition or papier-mâché child, all original. *H&J Foulke, Inc.*

Papier-mâché: Ca. 1920—on. Papier-mâché head and hands or arms, hard stuffed cloth body or full composition body; good hair wig, painted eyes, original child clothes; all in good condition of excellent quality.

4in (10cm)	**$45**
8—9in (20—23cm)	**65—75**
12in (31cm)	**90—100**
Gura: Ca. 1950. 13in (33cm)	**35—45**

Parian-Type
(Untinted Bisque)

Maker: Various German firms
Date: Ca. 1860s through 1870s
Material: Untinted bisque shoulder head, cloth or kid body, leather, wood, china or combination extremities
Mark: Usually none, sometimes numbers

Unmarked Parian: Pale or untinted shoulder head, sometimes with molded blouse, beautifully molded hairdo, (may have ribbons, beads, comb or other decoration), painted eyes, closed mouth; cloth body; lovely clothes; entire doll in fine condition.

16—18in (41—46cm)	$ 425—475
22—24in (56—61cm)	625—675
Very fancy hairdo and/or elaborately decorated blouse	700 up
Very fancy with glass eyes	1250 up
Common, plain style, 16in (41cm)	300
24in (61cm)	475
Alice hairdo with swivel neck,	
Motschmann-type body, 14in (36cm)	1600—1800**
"Augusta Victoria," 17in (43cm)	900
Swivel neck, blonde curls, ribbon, glass eyes, 22in (56cm)	2200
Alice hairdo, 21in (53cm)	750
Molded gray hat, white flowers, long blonde curls, 9in (23cm)	1450
Molded pink luster head piece, 18in (46cm)	1350

18in (46cm) Parian with pink lustre molded head piece. *Nancy Smith Collection.*

16in (41cm) Parian with molded braid in back. *Yvonne Baird Collection.*

Peg-Wooden or Dutch Dolls

Maker: Craftsmen of the Grödner Tal, Austria, and Sonneberg, Thüringia, Germany
Date: Late 18th—20th century
Material: All-wood, ball-jointed (larger ones) or pegged
Mark: None

Early to Mid 19th Century: Delicately carved head, varnished, carved and painted hair and features, with a yellow tuck comb in hair, painted spit curls, sometimes earrings; mortise and tenon peg joints; old clothes; all in fair condition.

8—9in (20—23cm)	**$ 850—900**
12—13in (31—33cm)	**1100—1200**
17—18in (43—46cm)	**1500—1600**
Swivel neck, molded bust, at auction	**4400**

Late 19th Century: Wooden head with painted hair, carving not so elaborate as previously, sometimes earrings, spit curls; dressed; all in good condition.

4in (10cm)	**$100**
8—10in (20—25cm)	**200—250**
12in (31cm)	**275—300**
Early 20th century:	
11—12in (28—31cm)	**50—75**

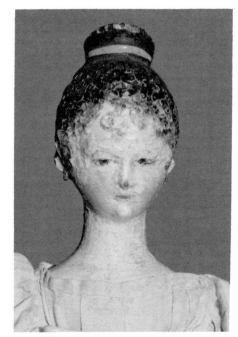

17½in (45cm) peg-wood with tuck comb, wearing original dress. *Elizabeth McIntyre.*

Dora Petzold

Maker: Dora Petzold, Berlin, Germany
Date: 1920—on
Material: Composition or cloth head, cloth body
Mark:

> "DORA PETZOLD
> Registered
> Trade Mark
> Doll
> Germany"

Dora Petzold Doll: Molded composition or cloth head with closed mouth, hair wig, pensive character face, painted features; cloth body sometimes with especially long arms and legs; dressed; all in good condition. Many unmarked.

20—28in (51—71cm)   **$800—900**

28in (71cm) Dora Petzold child. *Betty Harms Collection.*

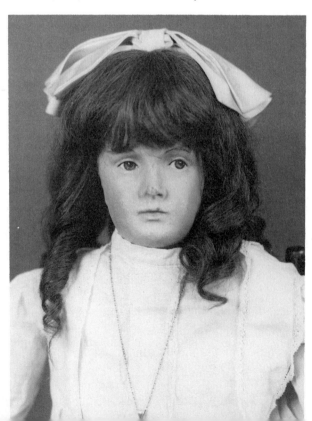

Phénix Bébé

Maker: Henri Alexandre, Paris, France; Torrel; Jules Steiner; Jules Mettais
Date: 1889—1900
Material: Bisque head, jointed composition body (sometimes one-piece arms and legs)
Designer: Henri Alexandre
Mark:

PHÉNIX
★95

Marked Bébé Phénix: 1889—1900. Perfect bisque head, French jointed body, sometimes with one-piece arms and legs; lovely old wig, bulbous set eyes, closed mouth, pierced ears; well dressed; all in good condition.

★ *92, 94, 95:*

12in (31cm)	$2250—2350
18—20in (46—51cm)	3000—3250
24—26in (61—66cm)	3700—4300

21in (53cm) *Phenix Bébé* incised "Modele ★ 92." *Betty Harms Collection.*

Philadelphia Baby

Maker: J. B. Sheppard & Co., Philadelphia, PA., U.S.A.
Date: Ca. 1900
Material: All-cloth
Size: 18—22in (46—56cm)
Mark: None

Philadelphia Baby: All-cloth with treated shoulder-type head, lower arms and legs; painted hair, well-molded facial features, ears; stocking body; good condition.

18—22in (46—56cm)	**$1600**
Fair condition, showing wear	**1000**
All original, mint condition	**2500**

Philadelphia Baby, totally original. See color photograph on page 195. *H&J Foulke, Inc.*

Piano Baby

Maker: Gebrüder Heubach, Kestner and other German makers
Date: 1880—on
Material: All-bisque
Size: Usually under 12in (31cm), some larger
Mark: Many unsigned; some with maker's particular mark

Piano Baby: All-bisque immobile with molded clothes and painted features; made in various sitting and lying positions. Heubach quality.

3—4in (8—10cm)	$125—150
7—8in (18—20cm)	275—325
11—12in (28—31cm)	500—600
Black, 3—4in (8—10cm)	125—150

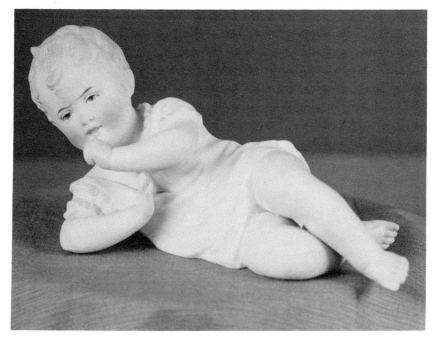

7½in (19cm) piano baby by Heubach. *H&J Foulke, Inc.*

Pincushion Dolls*

Maker: Various German firms, such as William Goebel, Dressel, Kister & Co.,
J.D. Kestner, Simon & Halbig, Limbach, Hertwig & Co., Gebrüder
Heubach

Date: 1900—on

Material: China, sometimes bisque

Size: Up to about 9in (23cm)

Mark: "Germany" and numbers

Pincushions: China half figures with molded hair and painted features; usually
with molded clothes, hats, lovely modeling and painting.

Arms close	**$ 30—40**
Arms extending but hands coming back to figure	**45 up**
Hands extended	**75 up**
Bisque child, glass eyes, 2in (5cm)	**175**
Painted eyes, 3in (8cm)	**125**
D&K Lady, large molded hat, extended arms, 9in (23cm) at auction	**1050**

*Also called half-dolls.

Marie Antoinette pincushion lady.
Catherine Magann.

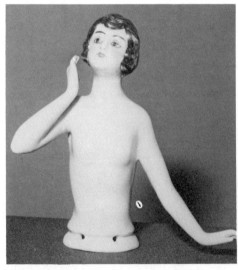

Nude flapper lady with extended arms.
Catherine Magann.

Pintel & Godchaux

Maker: Pintel & Godchaux, Montreuil, France
Date: 1890—1899
Material: Bisque head, jointed composition body
Trademark: Bébé Charmant
Mark:

B	A
P 9 G	P 7 G

Marked P.G. Doll: Perfect bisque head, paperweight eyes, closed mouth, good wig; jointed composition and wood body; appropriate clothing; all in good condition.

20—24in (51—61cm)	**$2500—3000**
Open mouth, 23in (58cm)	**1800—2000**

Open mouth P.G. Child. *Courtesy of Ann Dinnsen.*

Poir

Maker: Eugenie Poir, Paris, France and New York, NY; also Gre-Poir (French
    Doll Makers)
Date: 1920s
Material: All-cloth, felt face and limbs or all-felt
Mark: None on doll; paper label on clothes as below

Poir Child: All-fabric movable arms and legs; mohair wig; painted facial
    features; original clothes, all in good condition.
17—21in (43—53cm)   **$450—550**

18in (46cm) Poir *Rosette*, all original
with label. *H&J Foulke, Inc.*

Pre-Greiner
(So-called)

Maker: Unknown and various
Date: Ca. 1850
Material: Papier-mâché shoulder head, stuffed cloth body, mostly homemade, wood, leather or cloth extremities
Mark: None

Unmarked Pre-Greiner: Papier-mâché shoulder head; molded and painted black hair, pupil-less black glass eyes; cloth stuffed body, leather extremities; dressed in good old or original clothes; all in good condition.

20—24in (51—61cm)	**$ 900—1100**
28—32in (71—81cm)	**1500—1800**
Fair condition, much wear, 20—24in (51—61cm)	**650—750**

See color photograph on page 192.

Large pre-Greiner dolls with glass eyes. *Elizabeth McIntyre.*

Queen Anne-Type

Maker: English Craftsmen
Date: Late 17th—mid 19th century
Material: All-wood or wooden head and torso with leather or cloth limbs
Mark: None

Late 17th to Mid 18th Century: Carved wooden face, flax or hair wig, pupil-less glass eyes (sometimes painted), dotted eyebrows and eyelashes; jointed wooden body; old clothes, all in fair condition.

12—13in (31—33cm)	**$ 5,000 up**
18in (46cm)	**10,000 up**
24in (61cm)	**15,000 up**

Ca. 1690, 14½in (37cm), all original, fair condition, at auction **107,900**

Late 18th Century: Wooden head, gessoed, dotted eyelashes and eyebrows, glass eyes (later sometimes blue); pointed torso; old clothes; all in fair condition.

12—13in (31—33cm)	**$2500—3000**
16—18in (41—46cm)	**4500—5000**
24in (61cm)	**6000—6500**

Early 19th Century: Wooden head, gessoed, painted eyes, pointed torso, flax or hair wig; old clothes (dress usually longer than legs); all in fair condition.

18—20in (46—51cm) **$3000—3200**

12in (31cm) late 18th century Queen Anne with cloth arms, appropriately redressed. *Elizabeth McIntyre.*

Rabery & Delphieu

Maker: Rabery & Delphieu of Paris, France
Date: 1856 (founded)—1899—then with S. F. B. J.
Material: Bisque head, composition body
Mark: "R. D." (from 1890)
        On back of head:
        Body mark: 
(Please note last two lines illegible)

R $\frac{5}{0}$ D

BÉBÉ RABERY

Sᶜ ———

Marked R. D. Bébé: Ca. 1880s. Bisque head, lovely wig, paperweight eyes, closed mouth; jointed composition body; beautifully dressed; entire doll in good condition.

16—18in (41—46cm)	$2250—2450
23—27in (58—69cm)	3100—3700*

*For a lovely face.

See color photograph on page 70.

Raggedy Ann and Andy

Maker: Various
Date: 1915 to present
Material: All-cloth
Size: 4½—39in (12—99cm)
Creator: Johnny B. Gruelle

Early Raggedy Ann or Andy: All-cloth with movable arms and legs; brown yarn hair, button eyes, painted features; legs or striped fabric for hose and black for shoes; original clothes; all in fair condition.
MARK: "PATENTED SEPT. 7, 1915"
     (black stamp on front torso)
16in (41cm)   **$600—650**

Molly-'es Raggedy Ann or Andy: 1935—1938, manufactured by Molly-'es Doll Outfitters. Same as above, but with red hair and printed features; original clothes; all in good condition.
MARK:
          "Raggedy Ann and Raggedy Andy Dolls
          Manufactured by Molly'es Doll Outfitters"
          (printed writing in black on front torso)
16in (41cm)   **$300—350**

See color photograph on page 195.

Georgene Raggedy Ann or Andy: 1938-1963, manufactured by Georgene Novelties. Same as above, but with red hair and printed features; original clothes; all in good condition.
MARK: Cloth label sewn in side seam of body.
15—18in (38—46cm)   **$ 65—75**

Knickerbocker Toy Co. Raggedy Ann or Andy: 1963 to 1982.
12in (31cm)   **$ 20**
24in (61cm)   **85**
36in (91cm)   **125**

Applause Raggedy Ann and Andy, embroidered features. Available in toy stores.

Raleigh

Maker: Jessie McCutcheon Raleigh, Chicago, IL., U.S.A.
Date: 1916—1920
Material: All-composition or composition heads and cloth bodies
Designer: Jessie McCutcheon Raleigh
Mark: None

Raleigh Doll: Composition head, molded hair or wig, sleep or painted eyes; composition or cloth body; appropriate clothes; all in good condition.

12—13in (31—33cm)	**$375—400**
18in (46cm)	**500—550**

11½in (29cm) Raleigh girl, all original.
Leone McMullen Collection.

Raynal

Maker: Edouard Raynal, Paris, France
Date: 1922-on
Material: Felt and cloth, sometimes celluloid hands
Trademark: Poupées Raynal
Size: 17—18in (43—46cm)
Mark: "Raynal" on necklace or shoe soles

Raynal Doll: Molded felt mask face with mohair wig, beautifully painted eyes, closed lips, rosy cheeks; stuffed cloth body (may have celluloid hands); original clothes often of felt; all in good condition.
17—18in (43—46cm) **$500—600**

18in (46cm) unmarked doll which appears to be by Raynal. *H&J Foulke, Inc.*

Recknagel

Maker: Th. Recknagel, porcelain factory, Alexandrienthal, Thüringia,
Germany
Date: 1886—on
Material: Bisque head, composition or wood-jointed body
Size: Usually small
Mark: "R.A." with numbers, sometimes "Germany"

R. A. Child: Ca. 1890s-World War I. Perfect marked bisque head, jointed
composition or wooden body; good wig, set or sleep eyes, open mouth; some
dolls with molded painted shoes and socks; all in good condition.
1909, 1914, 1924:

8—9in (20—23cm)	**$125—150**
20—23in (51—58cm)	**350—400***

*Fine quality bisque only.

R. A. Character Baby: 1909-World War I. Perfect bisque socket head;
composition bent-limb baby or straight-leg curved-arm toddler body;
painted or glass eyes; nicely dressed; all in good condition. ***#127*** and others.

Infants, 8—9in (20—23cm)	**$200—250**
Character babies, ***#23*** and others,	
7—8in (18—20cm)	**275—300**
Bonnet babies, ***#22 & 28:***	
7—8in (18—20cm)	**325—375**

8in (20cm) R.A. pouty baby. *H&J Foulke, Inc.*

7in (18cm) R.A. 22 baby with molded bonnet. *Joanna Ott Collection.*

Grace Corry Rockwell

Maker: Unknown
Date: 1920s
Material: Bisque or composition head, cloth and composition body
Mark: Copr. by
            Grace C. Rockwell
            Germany

Grace Corry Child: 1927. ***Little Brother and Little Sister***. Averill Mfg. Co. Composition smiling face, molded hair, sometimes with wig, painted eyes, closed mouth; cloth and composition body; appropriate clothes; some with Madame Hendren labels; all in good condition. See *3rd Blue Book*, page 153.
14in (36cm)   **$400—450**

Grace Corry Rockwell Child: Perfect bisque head with molded hair or wig, sleep eyes, closed mouth; cloth and composition body; appropriate clothes; all in good condition.
14in (36cm)   **$3000 up****

**Not enough price samples to compute a reliable average.

14in (36cm) Grace Corry Rockwell child.
Esther Schwartz Collection.

Rohmer Fashion

Maker: Madame Marie Rohmer, Paris, France
Date: 1857—1880
Material: China or bisque shoulder head, jointed kid body
Mark:

Rohmer Fashion: China or bisque swivel shoulder head, jointed kid body, bisque or china arms, kid or china legs; lovely wig, set glass eyes, closed mouth, some ears pierced; fine costuming; entire doll in good condition.
16—20in (41—51cm) **$4000—5000**

Rohmer with china shoulder head and signed body. *Grace Dyar Antique Dolls.*

Rollinson Doll

Maker: Utley Doll Co., Holyoke, MA., U.S.A.
Date: 1916—on
Material: All-cloth
Size: 14—28in (36—71cm)
Designer: Gertrude F. Rollinson
Mark: Stamp in shape of a diamond with a doll in center, around border
"Rollinson Doll Holyoke, Mass."

Marked Rollinson doll: All molded cloth with painted head and limbs; painted hair or human hair wig, painted features (sometimes teeth also); dressed; all in good condition.

All sizes   **$ 900—975****

26in (66cm) wigged child, excellent, at auction   **2300**

**Not enough price samples to compute a reliable average.

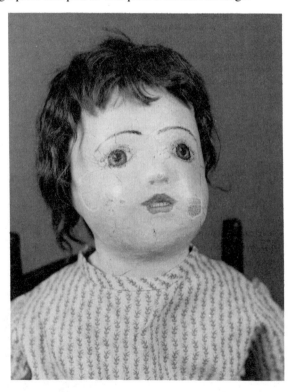

27in (69cm) Rollinson. *Betty Harms Collection.*

S.F.B.J.

Maker: Société Francaise de Fabrication de Bébés & Jouets, Paris, France
Date: 1899—
Material: Bisque head, composition body
Mark:

$$D\acute{E}\ POS\acute{E}$$
$$S.F.B.J.$$

Child Doll: 1899—on. Perfect bisque head, good French wig, set or sleep eyes, open mouth, pierced ears; jointed composition body; nicely dressed; all in good condition.

Jumeau-type (no mold number):
14—16in (36—41cm)	$ 800—900
20—22in (51—56cm)	1250—1500
25—27in (64—69cm)	1900—2100

#301:
14—16in (36—41cm)	650—750
20—22in (51—56cm)	825—875
25—27in (64—69cm)	1000—1200
30—32in (76—81cm)	1600—1800
Lady Body, 22in (56cm)	1100—1200

#60:
13—15in (33—38cm)	450—500
19—21in (48—53cm)	625—675
28in (71cm)	1000

Bleuette #301:
10in (25cm)	450—500
Walking, Kissing and Flirting: 22in (56cm)	1550—1650

10in (25cm) S.F.B.J. 301 child, possibly *Bleuette. Private Collection.*

S.F.B.J. continued

Character Dolls: 1910—on. Perfect bisque head, wig, molded, sometimes flocked hair on mold numbers ***237, 226, 227*** and ***235***, sleep eyes, composition body; nicely dressed; all in good condition.

#226, 235: 15—17in (38—43cm)	**$ 1650—1850**
13in (33cm) painted eyes	**1000**
#227, 237: 18—21in (46—53cm)	**2350—2650**
7in (18cm) baby, painted eyes	**500—550**
#230, (sometimes Jumeau):	
13in (33cm)	**1250**
Child, 20—22in (51—56cm)	**1800—2000**
#233: Screamer, 15in (38cm)	**2400****
#234: Baby, 15in (38cm)	**2600****
#236: Baby, 17—18in (43—46cm)	**1200—1400**
25in (64cm)	**2000**
Toddler, 14—15in (36—38cm)	**1500—1600**
27—28in (69—71cm)	**2300—2500**
#238, 229: Child, 15—16in (38—41cm)	**2600—2800**
Lady, 23—26in (58—66cm)	**3600—4000****
#239: Poulbot, 13in (33cm)	**19,000—21,000 pair**
#245: (See page 206)	
#247: Toddler, 16—18in (41—46cm)	**2300—2500**
27in (69cm)	**3200—3500**
#251: Baby, 19in (48cm)	**2000**
Toddler, 14—15in (36—38cm)	**1250—1350**
27—28in (69—71cm)	**2500—2700**
#252: Toddler, 18—20in (48—53cm)	**7000—7500**

**Not enough price samples to compute a reliable average.

For color photographs see pages 196 and 197.

15in (38cm) S.F.B.J. 229 character child. *Private Collection.*

17in (43cm) S.F.B.J. 235 character child. *Esther Schwartz Collection*

Sasha

Maker: Trendon Toys, Ltd., Rĕddish, Stockport, England
Date: 1965—1986
Material: All-vinyl
Designer: Sasha Morgenthaler

Sasha: All-vinyl of exceptionally high quality, long synthetic hair, painted features, wistful, appealing expression; original clothing, tiny circular wrist tag; excellent condition.

16in (41cm)	**$ 125—150**

Gregor (boy)	**150**
Cora (black girl)	**150—175**
Caleb (black boy)	**150—175**
Black Baby	**160—185**
White Baby	**125**
Sexed Baby	**150—175**
Limited Edition Dolls:	
1982 *Pintucks Dress*	**250**
1983 *Kiltie*	**250**
1985 *Prince Gregor*	**250**
1986 *Princess*	**1500 up**

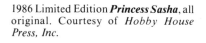

1986 Limited Edition *Princess Sasha*, all original. Courtesy of *Hobby House Press, Inc.*

Peter Scherf

Maker: Peter Scherf, doll factory, Sonneberg, Thüringia, Germany. Some heads by Armand Marseille.

Date: 1879—on

Material: Bisque head, kid or composition body

Size: Various

Mark:

Germany.
P. Sch. 1899-5/0

Made in Germany
P. Sch.
0.

Marked Scherf Doll: 1899—on. Perfect bisque head, set glass eyes, open mouth with teeth; kid or composition body; dressed; all in good condition. Mold numbers ***1899, 1901, 1902.***

Kid body,
   16—18in (41—46cm) $250—275
Composition body,
   14—16in (36—41cm)   250—275

15in (38cm) Peter Scherf child. *H&J Foulke, Inc.*

Bruno Schmidt

Maker: Bruno Schmidt, doll factory, Waltershausen, Thüringia, Germany.
Heads by Bähr & Pröschild, Ohrdruf, Thüringia, Germany.
Date: 1898—on
Material: Bisque head, composition body
Mark:

2096-4

Marked B. S. W. Child Doll: Ca. 1898—on. Bisque head, good wig, sleep eyes, open mouth; jointed composition child body; dressed; all in good condition.

19—21in (48—53cm)	**$450—500**
29—30in (71—76cm)	**850—950**
22in (56cm) flirty eyes,	**600**

Marked B. S. W. Character Dolls: Bisque socket head, glass eyes; jointed composition body; dressed; all in good condition.
#2048, 2094, 2096 (so-called *Tommy Tucker*), molded hair, open mouth, (For photograph see *7th Blue Book*, page 334.):

16—18in (41—46cm)	**$ 900—1100**
22—24in (56—61cm)	**1450—1650**

#2048 (closed mouth):
16—18in (41—46cm) **2000—2300**
#2072 17—19in (43—48cm) **2700—3200**
(For photograph see
7th Blue Book, page 335.)
#2033 (so-called *Wendy*): **3000—3500**
#2025 (529) closed mouth, wigged:
22in (56cm) **4300—4800**

22in (56cm) B. S. W. flirty-eyed child.
H&J Foulke, Inc.

Franz Schmidt

Maker: Franz Schmidt & Co., doll factory, Georgenthal near Waltershausen, Thüringia, Germany. Heads by Simon & Halbig, Grafenhain, Thüringia, Germany.

Date: 1890—on

Material: Bisque socket head, jointed bent-limb or toddler body of composition

Mark:

1295
F. S. & Co.
Made in
Germany
30

S & C
SIMON & HALBIG
28

Marked F.S. & Co. Character Baby: Ca. 1910. Perfect bisque character head, good wig, sleep eyes, open mouth, may have open nostrils; jointed bent-limb body; suitably dressed; all in good condition.

#1272, 1295, 1296, 1297, 1310:
Baby,

12—14in (31—36cm)	**$425—475**
18—20in (46—51cm)	**550—650**
24in (61cm)	**800—900**

Toddler,

7in (18cm)	**350—400**
9—10in (23—25cm)	**450—475**
16—17in (41—43cm)	**700—750**

Marked S & C Child Doll: Ca. 1890—on. Perfect bisque socket head, good wig, sleep eyes, open mouth; jointed composition child body; dressed; all in good condition. Some are Mold *#293.*

6—7in (15—18cm)	**$275—325**
14—16in (36—41cm)	**375—400**
23—25in (58—64cm)	**550—600**
42in (107cm)	**2700—2900**

36in (91cm) F.S. & Co. 1296 character boy. *India Stoessel Collection.*

6in (15cm) S & C 293 child. *H&J Foulke, Inc.*

Schmitt

Maker: Schmitt & Fils, Paris, France
Date: 1854—1891
Material: Bisque socket head, composition jointed body
Size: Various
Mark: On both head and body:

Marked Schmitt Bébé: Ca. 1879. Perfect bisque socket head with skin or good wig, large paperweight eyes, closed mouth, pierced ears; Schmitt-jointed composition body; appropriate clothes; all in good condition.

14—15in (36—38cm) $ **5300—5800**
23—24in (58—61cm) **10,000—12,000**
30—31in (76—79cm) **15,000—18,000**

24in (61cm) Schmitt bébé. *Kay and Wayne Jensen Collection.*

Schoenau & Hoffmeister

Maker: Schoenau & Hoffmeister, Porzellanfabrik Burggrub, Burggrub, Bavaria, Germany. Arthur Schoenau also owned a doll factory.

Date: 1884—on dolls; 1901—on porcelain

Material: Bisque head, composition body

Trademarks: Hanna, Burggrub Baby, Bébé Carmencita, Viola, Kunstlerkopf, Das Lachencle Baby.

Mark:

A S   S ⭐ H

Child Doll: 1901—on. Perfect bisque head; original or good wig, sleep eyes, open mouth; ball-jointed body; original or good clothes; all in nice condition. *#1909, 5500, 5800, 5700.* (For photograph see *7th Blue Book*, page 338.)

12—13in (31—33cm)	**$200—250**
17—19in (43—48cm)	**350—400**
24—26in (61—66cm)	**500—550**
30—31in (76—79cm)	**750—800**
Painted bisque, 13in (33cm)	**135—150**

Character Baby: 1910—on. Perfect bisque socket head, good wig, sleep eyes, open mouth; composition bent-limb baby body; all in good condition. *#169, 769,* "Burggrub Baby" or "Porzellanfabrik Burggrub."

13—15in (33—38cm)	**$350—400**
18—20in (46—51cm)	**475—525**
23—24in (58—61cm)	**650—750**

Hanna: (For photograph see *7th Blue Book*, page 339.)

Baby, 14—16in (36—41cm)	**$ 550—600**
23—26in (58—66cm)	**1000—1200**
Toddler, 11—12in (28—31cm)	**550—600**
16—18in (41—46cm)	**750—850**

Das Lachende Baby; 1930.

23—24in (58—61cm)	**$1750****

Princess Elizabeth, 1932. (For photograph see *7th Blue Book*, page 339.) Chubby five-piece body.

20—23in (51—58cm)	**$2400—3000**

**Not enough price samples to compute a reliable average.

Pouty Baby: Ca. 1925. Perfect bisque solid dome head with painted hair, tiny sleep eyes, closed pouty mouth; cloth body with composition arms and legs; dressed; all in good condition.

11—12in (28—31cm)	**$700—750****

**Not enough price samples to compute a reliable average.

Schoenau & Hoffmeister continued

23in (58cm) *Das Lachende Baby.*
Courtesy of Mary Pat Houston.

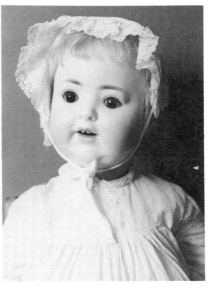

24in (61cm) Porzellanfabrik Burggrub
169 character baby. *H&J Foulke, Inc.*

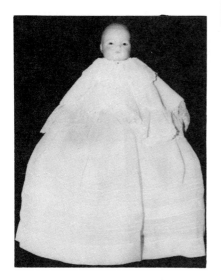

11in (28cm) S PB H pouty baby. *Lesley
Hurford Collection.*

Schoenhut

Maker: Albert Schoenhut & Co., Philadephia, PA., U.S.A.
Date: 1872—on
Material: Wood, spring-jointed, holes in bottom of feet to fit metal stand
Size: Various models 11—21in (28—53cm)
Designer: Early: Adolph Graziana and Mr. Leslie
　　　　　Later: Harry E. Schoenhut
Mark: Paper label:　　　　　　　　　　　　Incised:

SCHOENHUT DOLL
PAT. JAN. 17, '11, U.S.A.
& FOREIGN COUNTRIES

Character: 1911—1930. Wooden head and spring-jointed wooden body, marked head and/or body; original or appropriate wig, brown or blue intaglio eyes, open/closed mouth with painted teeth or closed mouth; original or suitable clothing; nothing repainted. Pouty or smiling.

14—21in (36—53cm)
　　Excellent condition　　　**$1300—1800***
　　Good, some wear　　　　**800—1000**

*Depending upon rarity of face.

See color photographs on pages 198 and 199.

Character with carved hair: Ca. 1911—1930. Wooden head with carved hair, comb marks, possibly a ribbon or bow, intaglio eyes, mouth usually closed; spring-jointed wooden body; original or suitable clothes.
14—21in (36—53cm):
　　Excellent condition　　**$1600—2000**
　　Good, some wear　　　**1100—1400**
　　Early style　　　　　　**2200—2500**
　　Molded cap　　　　　　**2200 up**

See color photographs on pages 198 and 200.

19in (48cm) #308 pouty girl, all original. *H&J Foulke, Inc.*

Schoenhut continued

Baby Face: Ca. 1913—1930. Wooden head and fully-jointed toddler or bent-limb baby body, marked head and/or body; painted hair or mohair wig, painted eyes, open or closed mouth; suitably dressed; nothing repainted; all in good condition.

MARK:

Baby,

12in (31cm)	$500
15—16in (38—41cm)	600—700

Toddler,

14in (36cm)	625—675
11in (28cm)	675—725
16—17in (41—43cm)	675—725

16in (41cm) Schoenhut baby. *H&J Foulke, Inc.*

Dolly Face: Ca. 1915—1930. Wooden head and spring-jointed wooden body; original or appropriate mohair wig, decal eyes, open/closed mouth with painted teeth; original or suitable clothes. (For photographs see *7th Blue Book*, page 343.)

14—21in (36—53cm) Excellent condition,	**$650—850**
Good condition, some wear,	**450—650**

Walker: Ca. 1919—1930. All-wood with "baby face," mohair wig, painted eyes; curved arms, straight legs with "walker" joint at hip; original or appropriate clothes; all in good condition. No holes in bottom of feet. (For photograph see *6th Blue Book*, page 334.)

13in (33cm)	**$600—700**

See color photograph on page 200.

Schoenhut continued

Sleep Eyes: Ca. 1920—1930. Used with "baby face" or "dolly face" heads. Mouths on this type were open with teeth or barely open with carved teeth.
14—21in (36—53cm) Excellent condition **$800—1000**
Good condition **700—800**

All-Composition: Ca. 1924. Jointed at neck, shoulders and hips, right arm bent, molded blonde curly hair, painted eyes, tiny closed mouth; original or appropriate clothing; in fair condition.
Paper label on back:
13in (33cm) **$350—400***

**Not enough price samples to compute a reliable range.

13in (33cm) all-composition Schoenhut girl, all original. See color photograph on page 199. *H&J Foulke, Inc.*

16in (41cm) Schoenhut girl with sleep eyes. *Yvonne Baird Collection.*

Schuetzmeister & Quendt

Maker: Schuetzmeister & Quendt, porcelain factory, Boilstadt, Thüringia, Germany, made heads for Welsch, Kämmer & Reinhardt, Wolf & Co.

Date: 1889
Material: Bisque head, composition body
Distributor: John Bing Co., New York, N.Y., U.S.A.

S & Q Child Doll: Ca. 1900. Perfect bisque head with mohair wig, sleep eyes, open mouth with teeth; jointed composition body; nicely dressed.

MARK:

S & Q
101
Dep.
6.

#101 Jeanette:
16—18in (41—46cm) $325—350
24—25in (61—64cm) 450—500

S & Q Character Baby: Ca. 1910. Perfect bisque head with mohair wig, sleep eyes, open mouth with tongue and teeth, slightly smiling; composition baby body; nicely dressed; all in good condition.

MARK:

301
S&Q
Germany

#201, 301:
12—13in (31—33cm) $300—350
19—21in (48—53cm) 550—600
24in (61cm)   700—750

Large S&Q character baby. *Richard Wright Antiques.*

Shirley Temple

Maker: Ideal Novelty Toy Corp., New York, N.Y., U.S.A.
Date: 1934 to present
Size: 7½—36in (19—91cm)
Designer: Bernard Lipfert
Mark: See individual doll listings below. (Ideal used marked Shirley Temple bodies for other dolls.)

All-Composition Child: 1934 through late 1930s. Marked head and body, jointed composition body; all original including wig and clothes; entire doll in very good condition. Came in sizes 11—27in (28—69cm)

MARK: On body: **SHIRLEY TEMPLE**
13

13

On head: **SHIRLEY TEMPLE**

On cloth label:

> *Genuine*
> SHIRLEY TEMPLE
> DOLL
> REGISTERED U.S. PAT OFF
> **IDEAL NOVELTY & TOY CO**
> MADE IN USA

11in (28cm)	$ 600—650*
13in (33cm)	500—550*
15—16in (38—41cm)	500—600*
18in (46cm)	550—650*
20—22in (51—56cm)	600—700*
25in (64cm)	750—800*
27in (69cm)	900—1000*
Button	75—85*
Dress	100 up
Trunk	100—125
"Shirley At Organ" Display piece	2000

18in (46cm) composition *Shirley Temple*, all original and boxed. *H&J Foulke, Inc.*

*Allow more for a mint-in-box doll or one with unusual outfit.

Shirley Temple continued

22in (56cm) composition **Shirley Temple**, all original. *H&J Foulke, Inc.*

Baby: 1934 through late 1930s. Composition swivel head with molded hair or blonde mohair wig, sleep eyes, open smiling mouth, dimples; cloth body, composition arms and legs; appropriate clothes; all in good condition. Came in six sizes, 16—25in (41—64cm). (For photograph see *7th Blue Book*, page 346.)

MARK: "Shirley Temple" on head

16—18in (41—46cm) **$850—900**

All-composition Shirley with molded hair: Late 1930s. Made in Japan.

7½in (19cm) **$225—250**

Hawaiian Shirley: Brown composition with black yarn hair, painted eyes; original grass skirt and ornaments; all in good condition.

13in (33cm)   **$500****
18in (46cm)   **750****

**Not enough price samples to compute a reliable average.

7½in (19cm) all-composition **Shirley Temple**, made in Japan. *H&J Foulke, Inc.*

Shirley Temple continued

Vinyl and Plastic: 1957. Vinyl and
plastic, rooted hair, sleep eyes;
jointed at shoulders and hips;
original clothes; all in excellent
condition. Came in sizes 12in
(31cm), 15in (38cm), 17in (43cm),
19in (48cm) and 36in (91cm)
MARK: "Ideal Doll ST—12"
(number denotes size)

12in (31cm)	**$ 150**
15in (38cm)	**225**
17in (43cm)	**275—325**
19in (48cm)	**350—375**
36in (91cm)	**1400**
12in (31cm) in boxed gift set	**275**

19in (48cm) 1957 vinyl ***Shirley Temple***,
all original. *H&J Foulke, Inc.*

Vinyl and Plastic: 1973. Vinyl and plastic, rooted hair, painted eyes, smiling
mouth; jointed shoulders and hips; original clothes; all in mint condition.
(For photograph see *4th Blue Book*, page 302.)

16in (41cm) size only	**$ 85—90**
Boxed	**125**
Boxed dresses	**30—35**

Simon & Halbig

Maker: Simon & Halbig, porcelain factory, Gräfenhain, Thüringia, Germany; purchased by Kämmer & Reinhardt in 1920

Date: 1869—on

Material: Bisque head, kid (sometimes cloth) or composition body

Mark:

S 13 H   1079-2
                DEP
    949   — S H
          Germany

Child doll with closed mouth:

Ca. 1879. Perfect bisque socket head on ball-jointed wood and composition body; good wig, glass eyes, closed mouth, pierced ears; dressed; all in good condition. (See *Simon & Halbig Dolls - The Artful Aspect* for photographs of mold numbers not shown here.)

#719, 749, 939, 949:

15—17in (38—43cm)	**$1650—1950**
20—23in (51—58cm)	**2250—2750**
27—29in (69—74cm)	**3250—3750**

#905, 908:

16—18in (41—46cm)	**2350—2650****

#929:

14in (36cm)	**1900—2000****

#720, 740, 950 (kid body):

9—10in (23—25cm)	**425—450**
18—20in (46—51cm)	**1300—1600**

#939, 949 (kid body):

20—22in (51—56cm)	**1500—1800**
27in (69cm)	**2500**

S.H. shoulder head (kid body):

15—17in (38—43cm)	**1300—1600****

****Not enough price samples to compute a reliable average.

15in (38cm) SH 8 on shoulder plate, swivel neck, closed mouth. *Private Collection.*

14in (36cm) S&H 939, closed mouth, composition body. *Private Collection.*

Simon & Halbig continued

All-Bisque Child: 1880—on. All-bisque child with swivel neck, pegged shoulders and hips; appropriate mohair wig, glass eyes, open or closed mouth; molded stockings and shoes.

#886 & 890:
Over-the-knee black or blue stockings. (For photograph see page 45.)

5½—6in (14—15cm)	$ 525—575*
7—7½in (18—19cm)	650—700*

Early model with five-strap bootines, closed mouth:

7—8in (18—20cm)	1000—1250*

*Allow extra for original clothes.

Child doll with open mouth and composition body: Ca. 1889 to 1930s. Perfect bisque head, good wig, sleep eyes, open mouth, pierced ears; original ball-jointed composition body; very pretty clothes; all in nice condition. See *Simon & Halbig Dolls - The Artful Aspect* for photographs of mold numbers not shown here.

#719, 739, 939, 949, 979:

14—16in (36—41cm)	$ 800—900
21—23in (53—58cm)	1150—1350
30—31in (76—79cm)	2300—2600

#540, 550, 1039, 1078, 1079, Baby Blanche:

12—14in (31—36cm)	350—450
17—19in (43—48cm)	450—500
22—24in (56—61cm)	550—650
28—30in (71—76cm)	900—1100
34—35in (86—89cm)	1700—2000
39—42in (99—107cm)	2700—3000

#1009:

19—21in (48—53cm)	650—750

7½in (19cm) all-bisque Simon & Halbig with beige five-strap boots, closed mouth. *Private Collection.*

#1248, 1249, Santa:

13—15in (33—38cm)	**625—700**
21—24in (53—61cm)	**900—1000**
26—28in (66—71cm)	**1400—1600**
37—38in (94—97cm)	**2550—2850**

#1039 key-wind walking body:

17—18in (43—46cm)	**1250**

#1039 walking, kissing:

20—22in (51—56cm)	**850—950**

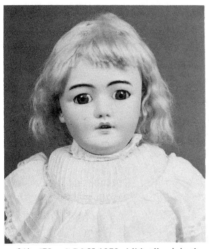

31in (79cm) S&H 1079 child, all original. *H&J Foulke, Inc.*

16in (41cm) S&H 1039 flirty-eye child. *Private Collection.*

24in (61cm) S&H **Baby Blanche**, walking body, mama box. *H&J Foulke, Inc.*

20in (51cm) S&H 1009 child. *Emma Wedmore Collection.*

Child doll with open mouth and kid body: Ca. 1889 to 1930s. Perfect bisque swivel head on shoulder plate or shoulder head with stationary neck, sleep eyes, open mouth, pierced ears; kid body, bisque arms, cloth lower legs; well costumed; all in good condition.

#1010, 1040, 1080:
14—16in	(36—41cm)	**$400—450**
21—23in	(53—58cm)	**550—600**

#1009 fashion-type body:
17—19in	(43—48cm)	**550—650**

#1250, 1260:
14—16in	(36—41cm)	**425—475**
22—24in	(56—61cm)	**700—750**

Tiny Child doll: Ca. 1889 to 1930s. Usually mold number **1079** or **1078**. Perfect bisque head, nice wig, sleep eyes, open mouth; composition body with molded shoes and socks; appropriate clothes; all in good condition.

7—8in	(18—20cm)	**$325—375**

Fully-jointed:
8—10in	(20—25cm)	**400—450**

8½in (22cm) S&H 1078, all original, fully-jointed body. *H&J Foulke, Inc.*

So-called Little Women type: Ca. 1900. Mold number **1160**. Shoulder head with fancy mohair wig, glass set eyes, closed mouth; cloth body with bisque limbs, molded boots; dressed; all in good condition.

5½—7in	(14—18cm)	**$325—375**
10—11in	(25—28cm)	**425—475**

Character Child: Ca. 1909. Perfect bisque socket head with wig or molded hair, painted or glass eyes, open or closed mouth, character face, jointed composition body; dressed; all in good condition. (See *Simon & Halbig Dolls - The Artful Aspect* for photographs of mold numbers not shown here.)

#120: 20—23in (51—58cm)		**$ 2200—2600**
#150: 20in (51cm)		**10,000**
#151: 18—20in (46—51cm)		**6500****
#153: 16in (41cm)		**7500 up****
#1279:		
9—10in (23—25cm)		**700—800**
16—18in (41—46cm)		**1400—1600**
23—25in (58—64cm)		**2400—2600**
#1299: 19—21in (48—53cm)		**900—1000**
#1339: 29in (74cm)		**1700****
#1388: 23in (58cm)		**10,000****
#1398: 23in (58cm)		**10,000****
#1478: 16—18in (41—46cm)		**6500 up****
IV, #1448: 18in (46cm)		**10,000 up****

**Not enough price samples to compute a reliable average.

Simon & Halbig continued

16in (41cm) S&H 1279
child. *Private Collection.*

Simon & Halbig continued

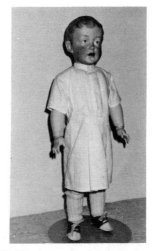

S&H 150 character, all original. *Joe Jackson/Joel Pearson.*

S&H 153 character. *Courtesy of Joan Eickelberg.*

Character Baby: Ca. 1909 to 1930s. Perfect bisque head, molded hair or wig, sleep or painted eyes, open or open/closed mouth; composition bent-limb baby or toddler body; nicely dressed; all in good condition. (See *Simon & Halbig Dolls - The Artful Aspect* for photographs of mold numbers not shown here.)

#1294:

Baby, 17—19in (43—48cm)	$ 600—700
23—25in (58—64cm)	900—1000
Toddler, 20in (51cm)	900

#1428:

Baby, 14in (36cm)	1000
Toddler, 14—16in (36—41cm)	1250—1500
25—27in (64—69cm)	2200—2500

#1488:

Toddler, 14—15in (36—38cm)	2700—2800
22in (56cm)	3300—3500

#1489, Erika:

Baby, 21—22in (53—56cm)	3000—3200
Toddler, 22in (56cm)	4300

#1498:

Toddler, 17in (43cm)	3000
Baby, 15in (38cm)	2000

27in (69cm) S&H 1488 character. *Esther Schwartz Collection.*

Simon & Halbig continued

S&H 1489 *Erika*. *Esther Schwartz Collection*.

27in (69cm) 1428 toddler. *Esther Schwartz Collection*.

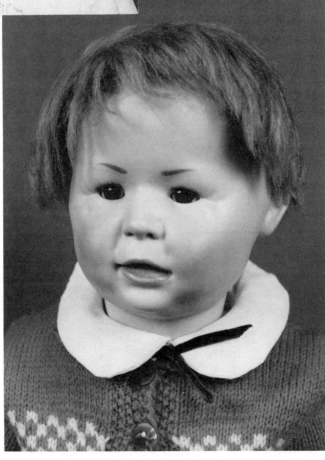

Simon & Halbig continued

Lady doll: Ca. 1910. Perfect bisque socket head, good wig, sleep eyes, pierced ears; lady body, molded bust, slim arms and legs; dressed; all in good condition.

#1159:

14in (36cm)	**$1000**
16—18in (41—46cm)	**1200—1400**
22in (56cm)	**2250**
26—27in (66—69cm)	**2500—2600**

#1469:

13—15in (33—38cm)	**1500—1600**

#1303:

15—16in (38—41cm)	**5000 up****

#152:

18in (46cm)	**8000 up****

**Not enough price samples to compute a reliable average.

17in (45cm) S&H 1159 with lady body.
H&J Foulke, Inc.

Snow Babies

Maker: Various German firms including Hertwig & Co. and Bähr & Pröschild
after 1910.
Date: Ca. 1890 until World War II
Material: All-bisque
Size: 1—3in (3—8cm) usually
Mark: Sometimes "Germany"

Snow Babies: All-bisque with snowsuits and caps of pebbly-textured bisque;
painted features; various standing, lying or sitting positions.

1½in (4cm)	**$ 30—35**
1½in (4cm) snow bear	**30—35**
1½in (4cm) snowman	**65—70**
3in (8cm) baby riding snow bear	**150—165**
2½in (6cm) tumbling snow baby	**100—110**
2in (5cm) musical snow baby	**65—75**
2in (5cm) baby on sled	**65—75**
3in (8cm) baby on sled	**125—135**
2in (5cm) reindeer pulling snow baby	**150—165**
2in (5cm) early fine quality babies with high hoods	**90—100**
3 small babies on sled	**125**
Santa on snow bear	**250—300**
3in (8cm) jointed snow baby	**225—275**
10in (25cm) snow baby shoulder head doll, cloth body, bisque limbs	**375—425**

10in (25cm) snow baby shoulder head
with molded pink ruffle around face.
Courtesy of Carolyn Guzzio.

3in (8cm) jointed and 2½in (6cm) standing
snow babies. *H&J Foulke, Inc.*

Sonneberg Täufling
(So-called Motschmann Baby)

Maker: Various Sonneberg factories such as Henrich Stier; many handled by exporter Louis Lindner & Söhn, Sonneberg, Thüringia, Germany
Date: 1851—1880s
Material: Papier-mâché, wood and cloth
Size: 8in (20cm) to about 28in (71cm)
Mark: None

Sonneberg Täufling: Papier-mâché or wax-over-composition head with painted hair or wig, glass eyes, closed mouth or open mouth with bamboo teeth; composition lower torso; composition arms and legs jointed at ankles and wrists, cloth covered midsection with voice box, upper arms and legs cloth covered, called floating joints; dressed in shirt and bonnet.

Very good condition:

12—14in (31—36cm)	**$ 450—500**
18—20in (46—51cm)	**650—850**
24in (61cm)	**1000**

Fair condition, with wear:

12—14in (31—36cm)	**350—400**
18—20in (46—51cm)	**550—650**
24in (61cm)	**800**

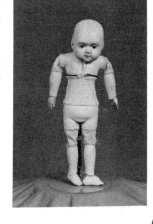

NOTE: For many years it was thought that these dolls were made by Ch. Motschmann, since some were found stamped with his name; hence, they were called ***Motschmann Babies*** by collectors. However, research has shown that they were made by various factories and that Motschmann was the holder of the patent for the voice boxes, not the manufacturer of the dolls.

ABOVE RIGHT: 14in (36cm) Sonneberg Täufling. *H&J Foulke, Inc.*

19in (48cm) Sonneberg Täufling with molded hair and sleep eyes. *Yvonne Baird Collection.*

Springfield Wooden Dolls

Maker: Jointed Doll Co. and D.M. Smith & Co., Springfield, V.T., U.S.A.
Date: 1879—1885
Material: Composition head over wooden core, fully-jointed wood body; hands and feet of pewter or lead
Size: Usually 12in (31cm)
Mark: Black paper band carrying patent dates fastened around the waist, but usually missing

---

Springfield Wooden Doll: Composition head-over-wood, fully-jointed wood body; metal hands and feet (usually); appropriate clothing; all in fair condition.
12in (31cm)   **$450—550**

12in (31cm) Springfield wooden doll. *Joanna Ott Collection.*

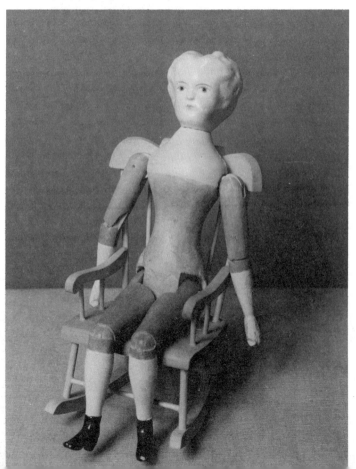

Steiff

Maker: Fraulein Margarete Steiff, Würtemberg, Germany
Date: 1894—on
Material: Felt, plush or velvet
Size: Various
Mark: Metal button in ear

Steiff Doll: Felt, plush or velvet, jointed; seam down middle of face, button eyes, painted features; original clothes; most are character dolls, many have large shoes to enable them to stand; all in good condition.

Children (Character Dolls):

11—12in (28—31cm)$	**850**	
16—17in (41—43cm)	**1200—1400**	

Caricature or Comic

Dolls:	**1100—3000**
18in (46cm) Soldiers	**3000**
16in (41cm) Chef	**1700**
14in (36cm) Cobbler	**1500**
18in (46cm) Dutch	**2300**
8in (20cm) Nazi boy	**1300**
8in (20cm) Elf	**1100**
18in (46cm) Lady	**1500**
Set of 4 18in (46cm)	
Musicians, at auction	**10350**

See color photographs on pages 276 and 277.

ABOVE RIGHT: 13½in (34cm) Steiff character girl, all original. *Kay & Wayne Jensen Collection.*

20in (51cm) Steiff sailor caricature, all original. *Nancy Smith Collection.*

E.U. Steiner

Maker: Edmund Ulrich Steiner, doll factory, Sonneberg, Thüringia, Germany
Date: 1864—on
Material: Bisque heads, kid, cloth or composition body
Trademark: Magestic
Mark:

E.U. Steiner Child Doll: Ca. 1902. Perfect bisque head, original or appropriate wig, sleep or set glass eyes, open mouth; ball-jointed composition body or kid body; appropriately dressed; entire doll in good condition.

Kid body:

14—16in (36—41cm) **$200—225**
22—24in (56—61cm) **325—375**

Composition body:

15—17in (38—43cm) **300—350**
21—23in (53—58cm) **400—450**

23in (58cm) E.U. Steiner child. See color photograph on page 277. *H&J Foulke, Inc.*

Jules Steiner

Maker: Jules Nicholas Steiner and Successors, Paris, France
Date: 1855—1908
Material: Bisque head, jointed papier-mâché body
Size: Various
Mark: Various as shown below

Marked Bourgoin Steiner Bébé: Ca. 1880. Perfect socket head, cardboard
pate, appropriate wig, sleep eyes with wire mechanism, bulgy paperweight
eyes with tinting on upper eyelids, closed mouth, round face, pierced ears
with tinted tips; jointed composition body; dressed; all in good condition.
Sometimes with wire-operated sleep eyes. "C" or "A" Series.

MARK: (incised)

S^{TE} A O

(red script)

I Steiner. Bte S.g. Bg. I Bourgoin Sie

14in (36cm)	$3500—3600
17—18in (43—46cm)	4000—4400
24in (61cm)	5000—5500

16½in (42cm) Bourgoin Steiner "C"
Series, all original except wig. *Private
Collection.*

Jules Steiner continued

Round face with open mouth: Ca. 1870s. Perfect very pale bisque socket head, appropriate wig, bulgy paperweight eyes, open mouth with pointed teeth, round face, pierced ears; jointed composition body; dressed; all in good condition.

MARK: None, but sometimes body has a label

Two rows of teeth,
  18—20in (46—51cm)**$2600—2800**
Kicking, crying bébé,
  mechanical key-wind body
  with composition arms
  and lower legs,
  20—22in (51—56cm) **1800—2100**
Motschmann-type body with
  bisque shoulders, hips and
  lower arms and legs. (For photograph see *7th Blue Book*, page 361.)
  18—21in (46—53cm) **4000—4500****

Early Steiner with two rows of teeth. *Private Collection.*

**Not enough price samples to compute a reliable range.

"C" Series Bebe: Ca. 1880. Perfect bisque socket head, cardboard pate, appropriate wig, sleep eyes with wire mechanism or paperweight eyes, closed mouth, full cheeks, pierced ears; jointed composition body; dressed; all in good condition.

MARK:

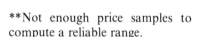

S^{TE} C 4 (incised)

J. STEINER B. S.G. D.G. (red stamp)
  14—16in (36—41cm) **$3500—3800**
  21—23in (53—58cm) **4800—5300**
  29—30in (74—76cm) **7500—8000**

18½in (47cm) Steiner (red stamp) with bisque hands. *Kay & Wayne Jensen Collection.*

Jules Steiner continued

"A" Series Bébé: Ca. 1885. Perfect bisque socket head, cardboard pate, appropriate wig, paperweight eyes, closed mouth, pierced ears; jointed composition body; dressed; all in good condition.

MARK: (incised)   J. STEINER
Bᵀᴱ S.G.D.G.
PARIS
Fⁱᴿᴱ A 15

Body and/or head may be stamped:
"Le Petit Parisien
BEBE STEINER
MEDAILLE d'OR
PARIS 1889"
or paper label of doll carrying
flag

8in (20cm)	**$2200—2400**
12—13in (31—33cm)	**2300—2600**
17—18in (43—46cm)	**3500—4000**
23—25in (58—64cm)	**5000—6000**
29in (74cm)	**7500—8500**

12½in (32cm) Steiner Fire A-5. *Private Collection.*

Bébé Le Parisien: Ca. 1892. Perfect bisque socket head, cardboard pate, appropriate wig, paperweight eyes, closed or open mouth, pierced ears; jointed composition body; dressed; all in good condition.

MARK: head (incised):
A - 19
(red stamp):   PARIS
"LE PARISIEN"
body (purple stamp):
"BEBE 'LE PARISIEN'
MEDAILLE D'OR
PARIS"

Closed mouth:

13—15in (33—38cm)	**$2600—3000**
18—20in (46—51cm)	**3600—4200**
23—25in (58—64cm)	**4800—5500**

Open mouth:

20—22in (51—56cm)	**2500**

23in (58cm) Steiner A-15. *Kay & Wayne Jensen Collection.*

Swaine & Co.

Maker: Swaine & Co., porcelain factory, Hüttensteinach, Sonneberg, Thüringia, Germany
Date: Ca. 1910—on for doll heads
Material: Bisque socket head, composition baby body
Mark: Stamped in green:

Incised Lori: Perfect bisque solid dome head, painted hair, sleep eyes, closed mouth; composition baby body with bent limbs; dressed; all in good condition.

22in (56cm)   **$2800**

#232

(open-mouth ***Lori***):
19—23in (48—58cm) **1500—1800**

DIP, F.P.:

(wig, glass eyes, closed mouth):
12in (31cm)   **800**
16—18in (41—46cm) **1150—1350**

DV:

(molded hair, glass eyes
open/closed mouth):
14—16in (36—41cm)   **900—1000**

DI, F O, A:

(molded hair, intaglio eyes,
open/closed mouth):
14—16in (36—41cm)   **800—900**

B.P., B.O.:

(smiling character):
16—18in (41—46cm) **3500—3800****

**Not enough price samples to compute a reliable range

13½in (34cm) DI character baby. *Esther Schwartz Collection.*

17in (43cm) DIP character toddler. *Kay & Wayne Jensen Collection.*

Terri Lee

Maker: TERRI LEE Sales Corp., V. Gradwohl, Pres., U.S.A.
Date: 1946-Lincoln, NE; then Apple Valley, CA. from 1951-Ca. 1962
Material: First dolls, rubbery plastic composition; later, hard plastic
Size: 16in (41cm) and 10in (25cm)
Mark: embossed across shoulders
First dolls:

"TERRI LEE
PAT. PENDING"

raised letters
Later dolls: "TERRI LEE"

Terri Lee Child Doll: Original wig, painted eyes; jointed at neck, shoulders and hips; all original clothing and accessories; very good condition.

16in (41cm):

Early model	**$200—250**
Hard plastic	**150—200**
Jerri Lee,	
16in (41cm)	**200**
Tiny Terri Lee, inset eyes,	
10in (25cm)	**125—135**
Tiny Jerri Lee, inset eyes,	
10in (25cm)	**185**
Connie Lynn	**350**
Linda Baby	**150—175**
Gene Autry	**500 up****

**Not enough price samples to compute a reliable range.

16in (41cm) ***Terri Lee***, all original. *H&J Foulke, Inc.*

10in (25cm) ***Tiny Terri Lee***, all original. *H&J Foulke, Inc.*

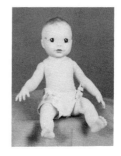

Linda Baby. *H&J Foulke, Inc.*

Unis

Maker: Société Française de Fabrication de Bébés et Jouets.
(S. F. B. J.) of Paris and Montruil-sous-Bois, France
Date: 1922—on
Material: Bisque head, composition body
Size: 5in (13cm) up
Mark:

71 UNIS FRANCE 149
301

Unis Child Doll: Perfect bisque head, wood and composition jointed body;
good wig, sleep eyes, open mouth; pretty clothes; all in nice condition.
#301 or 60 (fully jointed body):

8—10in (20—25cm)	**$ 350—400**
15—17in (38—43cm)	**500—550**
23—25in (58—64cm)	**700—800**

Costume Doll, five-piece body:

5in (13cm)	**150—200**
11—13in (28—33cm)	**275—325**
Black or brown bisque, 11—13in (28—33cm)	**325—375**

Princess: See page 247.
#251 character toddler:

14—15in (36—38cm)	**1100—1200**

#272 Baby:

17in (43cm)	**600****

Composition head 301 or 60:

11—13in (28—33cm)	**150—175**

**Not enough price samples to compute a reliable range.

8in (20cm) Unis 60 child. *H&J Foulke, Inc.*

5in (13cm) Unis 301 costume doll, all original. *H&J Foulke, Inc.*

Verlingue

Maker: J. Verlingue of Boulogne-sur-Mer, France
Date: 1914—1921
Material: Bisque head, composition body
Size: Various
Mark:

Marked J. V. Child: Perfect bisque head, good wig, glass eyes, open mouth; jointed papier-mâché body; nicely dressed.
15—17in (38—43cm) **$500—550**
22—24in (56—61cm) **750—850**

Verlingue All-bisque Doll: Head with wig, swivel neck, sleep eyes, closed mouth; jointed shoulders and hips; long painted hose, garters, black boots; undressed; mediocre quality.
7in (18cm) **$250—300**

17in (43cm) *Liane* child. *Dr. Carole Stoessel Zvonar Collection.*

Vogue-Ginny

Maker: Vogue Dolls, Inc.
Date: 1937—on
Material: 1937—1948 composition, 1948—1962 hard plastic
Size: 7—8in (18—20cm)
Creator: Jennie Graves
Clothes Designer: Virginia Graves Carlson
Clothes Label: "Vogue," "Vogue Dolls," or

> VOGUE DOLLS, INC.
> MEDFORD, MASS. USA
> ® REG U.S. PAT OFF

All-composition Toddles: Jointed neck, shoulders and hips; molded hair or mohair wig, painted eyes looking to side; original clothes; all in good condition.

MARK: "VOGUE" on head
"DOLL CO." on back
"TODDLES" stamped
on sole of shoe

7—8in (18—20cm)   **$175—225***

*Allow extra for mint condition.

Vogue *Toddles*, all original except footwear. *H&J Foulke, Inc.*

Hard Plastic Ginny: All-hard plastic, jointed at neck, shoulders and hips (some have jointed knees and some walk); nice wig, sleep eyes (early ones have painted eyes, later dolls have molded eyelashes); original clothes; all in excellent condition with perfect hair and pretty coloring.

MARK: On strung dolls:
"VOGUE DOLLS"
On walking dolls:
"GINNY//VOGUE DOLLS"

7—8in (18—20cm):

1948—1949:	
Painted eyes	$ 250—350*
Separate outfits	50—65
1950—1953:	
Painted eyelashes, strung,	225—275*
Separate outfits	50—65
1954:	
Painted eyelashes, walks	175—225*
Caracul wig	325—350
Separate outfits	45—55
1955—1957:	
Molded eyelashes, walks	135—175*
Separate outfits	40—50
1957—1962:	
Molded eyelashes, walks, jointed knees	115—140*
Separate outfits	30—40

Vogue-Ginny continued

1963—1965:
Vinyl head, hard plastic body,
jointed knees **85—95**
Black Ginny **750 up**
Coronation Ginny **1000 up**
Wee Imp **160—210**

*Allow extra for special outfits.

Hard Plastic Ginny Baby: Bent
limbs, jointed at neck, shoulders
and hips; caracul wig, painted or
sleep eyes; original clothes; all in
good condition. (For photograph
see *7th Blue Book*, page 369.)
8in (20cm)
Crib Crowd **$550**
Easter Bunny **650 up**

Vogue *Ginny* with molded lashes, all
original. *H&J Foulke, Inc.*

Vogue *Toddles Jill*, with painted lash *Ginnys*. *Beth Foulke Collection.*

WPA

Maker: Various artists under the sponsorship of the Works Projects Administration

Date: 1935—1943

Mark: Usually a number and location, such as "#7040, Milwaukee, Wis."

WPA Milwaukee Cloth doll: Stockinette head doll with yarn hair, molded face, painted features; cloth body; appropriate clothes; all in very good condition. (For photograph see *6th Blue Book*, page 361.)

22—23in (56—59cm)   **$1100—1300**

Molded composition-type doll: Finely molded individual faces, unjointed adult bodies; lovely authentic clothing representing various nationalities.

16in (41cm)   **$650 pair****

**Not enough price samples to compute a reliable range.

Plaster composition heads: Molded heads with little original detail, cloth bodies; original regional costumes.

12in (31cm)   **$25—35 each**

16in (41cm) WPA dolls with finely molded features, authentic clothing. *Esther Schwartz Collection.*

Wagner & Zetzsche

Maker: Wagner & Zetzsche, doll factory, Ilmenau, Thüringia, Germany. Bisque heads by porcelain factories including Gebrüder Heubach and Alt, Beck & Gottschalck

Date: 1875—on

Material: Bisque head, cloth, kid or composition body, celluloid-type heads

---

Closed-mouth Child: Ca. 1880s. Perfect turned bisque shoulder head with solid dome (mold **639**) or open crown (mold **698**), sometimes with plaster dome, mohair wig, paperweight eyes (a few with sleep eyes), flat eyebrows, closed mouth, small ears; kid or cloth body with bisque hands; appropriate clothes; all in good condition. (See photograph on page 279.)

    MARK: Blue paper body label with "W Z" initials entwined in fancy scroll.

15—17in (38—43cm) **$ 550—600**
20—22in (51—56cm)   **700—800**
26in (66cm)   **1000**

Character Baby or Child: Ca. 1910. Perfect bisque socket head, wig, sleep eyes, open mouth with upper teeth; dressed; all in good condition.
    MARK:

#10586 made by Gebrüder
  Heubach:
Baby body,
  16—18in (41—46cm) **$525—575**
Kid and composition body,
  14—16in (36—41cm)   **400—450**
#10585 (shoulder head, kid body):
  16—18in (41—46cm)   **325—375**

Portrait Children: 1915—on. Celluloid-type head (*Haralit*) with molded hair, painted eyes. Portraits of the children of Max Zetzsche: *Harold, Hansi,* and *Inge*.

    MARK: "Harald
           W.Z."
         (or name of child)

14in (36cm) *Harald*. (For photograph see *6th Blue Book*, page 363.)
  Fair condition   **$250****
8in (20cm) *Hansi*   **125****
Inge, 1924, 14in (36cm). (See color photograph on page 279.)
  Excellent   **450****

**Not enough price samples to compute a reliable range.

Wagner & Zetzsche continued

17in (43cm) Gebrüder Heubach *10585*
shoulder head for Wagner and Zetzsche.
H&J Foulke, Inc.

Izannah Walker

Maker: Izannah Walker, Central Falls, R.I., U.S.A.
Date: 1873, but probably made as early as 1840s
Material: All-cloth
Size: 15—30in (38—76cm)
Mark: Later dolls are marked: " *Patented Nov. 4th 1873* "

Izannah Walker Doll: Stockinette, pressed head, features and hair painted
with oils, applied ears, treated limbs; muslin body; appropriate clothes; in
good condition.

17—19in (43—48cm)   **$12,000—15,000**
Fair condition, 18in (46cm)   **8000**

18in (46cm) Izannah Walker, restored face. *Betty Harms Collection.*

Wax Doll, Poured

Maker: Various firms in London, England, such as Montanari, Pierotti, Peck, Meech, Marsh, Morrell, Cremer and Edwards
Date: 1850s through the early 1900s
Material: Wax head, arms and legs, cloth body
Mark: Sometimes stamped on body with maker or store

Poured Wax Child: Head, lower arms and legs of wax; cloth body; set-in hair, glass eyes; original clothes or very well dressed; all in good condition.

17—19in (43—48cm)	**$1250—1550**
24—26in (61—66cm)	**1750—2000**
Lady, 22—24in (56—61cm)	**1550—1850**
Man, 18in (46cm) inset mustache	**1650**

18in (46cm) Charles Morrell poured wax. *Yvonne Baird Collection.*

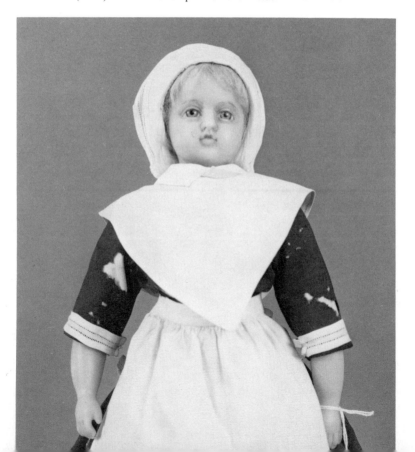

Wax-Over-Composition

Maker: Numerous firms in England, Germany or France
Date: During the 1800s
Material: Wax-over-shoulder head of some type of composition or papier-mâché, cloth body, wax-over-composition or wooden limbs
Mark: None

English Slit-head Wax: Ca. 1830—1860. Wax-over-shoulder head, not rewaxed; human hair wig, glass eyes (may open and close by a wire), faintly smiling; original cloth body with leather arms; original or suitable old clothing; all in fair condition, showing wear. (For photograph see *6th Blue Book*, page 366.)

12—14in (31—36cm)   **$300—350**
20—22in (51—56cm)   **550—600**

Molded Hair Doll: Ca. 1860—on. German wax-over-shoulder head, not rewaxed; molded hair sometimes with bow, glass sleep or set eyes; original cloth body; wax-over or wooden extremities with molded boots or bare feet; nice old clothes; all in good condition, good quality.

14—16in (36—41cm)   **$250—300**
22—25in (56—64cm)   **450—500**

25in (64cm) wax-over doll with molded hair, all original. *H&J Foulke, Inc.*

Wax Over Composition continued

22in (56cm) wax-over boy. *H&J Foulke, Inc.*

20in (51cm) wax-over doll with wig, superior quality. *Yvonne Baird Collection.*

Wax Doll With Wig: Ca. 1860s to 1900. German. Wax-over-shoulder head, not rewaxed; blonde or brown human hair or mohair wig, blue, brown or black glass eyes, sleep or set, open or closed mouth; original cloth body, any combination of extremities mentioned above, also arms may be made of china; original clothing or suitably dressed; entire doll in nice condition.

Standard quality:

11—12in (28—31cm)	**$ 125—150**	
16—18in (41—46cm)	**300—325**	
22—24in (56—61cm)	**400—450**	

Superior quality (heavily waxed):

11—12in (28—31cm)	**200—250**	
16—18in (41—46cm)	**400—450**	
22—24in (56—61cm)	**600—650**	
30in (76cm) excellent, all original at auction	**1200**	

Bonnet Wax Doll: Ca. 1860 to 1880. Wax-over-shoulder head, with molded bonnet; molded hair may have some mohair or human hair attached, blue, brown or black set eyes; original cloth body and wooden extremities; nice old clothes; all in good condition. (For photograph see *5th Blue Book*, page 339.)

16—17in (41—43cm) **$1750****

**Not enough price samples to compute a reliable range.

Double-Faced Doll: 1880—on. Fritz Bartenstein. One face crying, one laughing, rotating on a vertical axis by pulling a string, one face hidden by a hood. Body stamped "Bartenstein."

15—16in (38—41cm) **$850**

Norah Wellings

Maker: Victoria Toy Works, Wellington, Shropshire, England, for Norah Wellings
Date: 1926—Ca. 1960
Material: Fabric: Felt, velvet and velour, and other material, stuffed
Designer: Norah Wellings
Mark: On tag on foot: "Made in England by Norah Wellings"

Wellings Doll: All-fabric, stitch-jointed shoulders and hips; molded fabric face (also of papier-mâché, sometimes stockinette covered), painted features; all in excellent condition. Most commonly found are sailors, Canadian Mounties, Scots and Black Islanders.

Characters (floppy limbs):

8—10in (20—25cm)	**$ 50—75**	
13—14in (33—36cm)	**110—135**	
Glass eyes,		
14in (36cm)		
Black	**160—185**	

Children:

12—13in (31—33cm)	**325—375**	
16—18in (41—46cm)	**450—550**	
23in (58cm)	**850**	
Glass eyes,		
16—18in (41—46cm)	**550—650**	

Norah Wellings *Little Pixie People*. *Esther Schwartz Collection.*

Norah Wellings novelty dolls as shown on box lid. *Esther Schwartz Collection.*

ABOVE LEFT: 12in (31cm) Norah Wellings child, all original. *Esther Schwartz Collection.*

ABOVE RIGHT: 15in (38cm) Norah Wellings Spanish costume child. *Esther Schwartz Collection.*

Wislizenus

Maker: Adolf Wislizenus, doll factory, Waltershausen, Thüringia, Germany. Heads made by Bähr & Pröschild, Simon & Halbig and Ernst Heubach.

Date: 1851—on

Material: Bisque head, composition ball-jointed body

Trademarks: Old Glory, Special, Queen Quality

Mark:

Germany

A.W.

☐

Wislizenus Child Doll: Ca. 1890—on. Perfect bisque head, composition ball-jointed body; good wig; blue or brown sleep eyes, open mouth; dressed; all in good condition.

17—19in (43—48cm) **$350—400**
23—25in (58—64cm)   **450—500**

Wislizenus Character Doll: Perfect bisque socket head, molded hair, painted eyes, open/closed mouth with molded teeth; composition toddler body; dressed; all in good condition.

#110 or *115:*
16—18in (41—46cm) **$800—1000**

Marked A.W. Character: Perfect bisque socket head, good wig, sleep eyes, open/closed mouth with molded tongue and two separated porcelain teeth; bent-limb baby body. (For photograph see *7th Blue Book*, page 379.)
26in (66cm) **$1200—1300****

**Not enough price samples to compute a reliable range.

15in (38cm) A.W. 110 toddler. *H&J Foulke, Inc.*

Wood, German

Maker: Various companies, such as Rudolf Schneider and Schilling, Sonne-
berg, Thüringia, Germany
Date: 1901—1914
Material: All-wood, fully-jointed or wood head and limbs, cloth body
Mark: Usually none; sometimes Schilling "winged angel" trademark

---

*"Bébé Tout en Bois" (Doll all of
Wood):* All of wood, fully-jointed; wig, inset glass eyes, open
mouth with teeth; appropriate
clothes; all in fair to good condition.
10—13in (25—33cm) **$300—400**
17—19in (43—48cm) **500—600**
22—24in (56—61cm) **750**

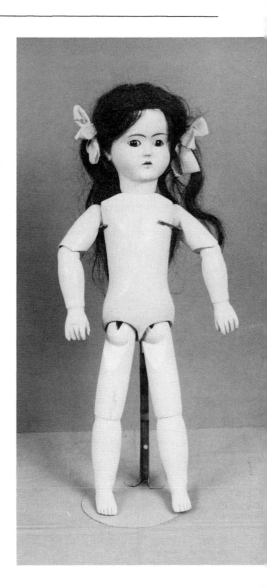

24in (61cm) *Bébé Tout en Bois.* H&J
Foulke, Inc.

Wood, Swiss

Maker: Various Swiss firms
Date: 20th century
Material: All-wood or wood head and limbs on cloth body
Size: Various, but smaller sizes are more commonly found
Mark: Usually a paper label on wrist or clothes

Swiss Wooden Doll: Wooden head with hand-carved features and hair
with good detail (males sometimes have carved hats); all carved wood jointed
body; original, usually regional attire; excellent condition.

9—10in (23—25cm)	**$185—225**
12in (31cm)	**250—275**
18in (46cm)	**500—550**

See color photograph on page 120.

9in (23cm) Swiss wood with carved hair
in original Bern costume. *H&J Foulke,
Inc.*

Glossary

Applied Ears: Ear molded independently and affixed to the head. (On most dolls the ear is included as part of the head mold.)

Bald Head: Head with no crown opening, could be covered by a wig or have painted hair.

Ball-jointed Body: Usually a body of composition or papier-mâché with wooden balls at knees, elbows, hips and shoulders to make swivel joints.

Bébé: French child doll with "dolly face."

Belton-type: A bald head with one, two or three small holes for attaching wig.

Bent-limb Baby Body: Composition body of five pieces with chubby torso and curved arms and legs.

Biskoline: Celluloid-type of substance for making dolls.

Bisque: Unglazed porcelain, usually flesh tinted, used for dolls' heads or all-bisque dolls.

Breather: Dolls with an actual opening in each nostril; also called open nostrils.

Breveté (or Bté):   Used on French dolls to indicate that the patent is registered.

Character Doll: Dolls with bisque or composition heads, modeled to look lifelike, such as infants, young or older children, young ladies and so on.

China: Glazed porcelain used for dolls' heads and *Frozen Charlottes*.

Child Dolls: Dolls with a typical "dolly face" which represent a child.

Composition: A material used for dolls' heads and bodies, consisting of such items as wood pulp, glue, sawdust, flour, rags and sundry other substances.

Contemporary Clothes: Clothes not original to the doll, but dating from the same period when the doll would have been a plaything.

Crown Opening: The cut-away part of a doll head.

DEP: Abbreviation used on German and French dolls claiming registration.

D.R.G.M.:   Abbreviation used on German dolls indicating a registered design or patent.

Dolly Face: Typical face used on bisque dolls before 1910 when the character face was developed; "dolly faces" were used also after 1910.

Embossed Mark: Raised letters, numbers or names on the backs of heads or bodies.

Feathered Eyebrows: Eyebrows composed of many tiny painted brush strokes to give a realistic look.

Fixed Eyes: Glass eyes which do not move or sleep.

Flange Neck: A doll's head with a ridge at the base of the neck which contains holes for sewing the head to a cloth body.

Flapper Dolls: Dolls of the 1920s period with bobbed wig or molded hair and slender arms and legs.

Flirting Eyes: Eyes which move from side to side as doll's head is tilted.

Frozen Charlotte: Doll molded all in one piece including arms and legs.

Ges. (Gesch.):   Used on German dolls to indicate design is registered or patented.

Googly Eyes: Large, often round, eyes looking to the side; also called roguish or goo goo eyes.

Hard Plastic: Hard material used for making dolls after 1948.

Incised Mark: Letters, numbers or names impressed into the bisque on the back of the head or on the shoulder plate.

Intaglio Eyes: Painted eyes with sunken pupil and iris.

JCB: Jointed composition body. See *ball-jointed body.*

Kid Body: Body of white or pink leather.

Lady Dolls: Dolls with an adult face and a body with adult proportions.

Mohair: Goat's hair widely used in making doll wigs.

Molded Hair: Curls, waves and comb marks which are actually part of the mold and not merely painted onto the head.

Motschmann-type Body: Doll body with cloth midsection and upper limbs with floating joints; hard lower torso and lower limbs.

Open-Mouth: Lips parted with an actual opening in the bisque, usually has teeth either molded in the bisque or set in separately and sometimes a tongue.

Open/Closed Mouth: A mouth molded to appear open, but having no actual slit in the bisque.

Original Clothes: Clothes belonging to a doll during the childhood of the original owner, either commercially or homemade.

Painted Bisque: Bisque covered with a layer of flesh-colored paint, which has not been baked in, so will easily rub or wash off.

Paperweight Eyes: Blown glass eyes which have depth and look real, usually found in French dolls.

Papier-mâché: A material used for dolls' heads and bodies, consisting of paper pulp, sizing, glue, clay or flour.

Pate: A shaped piece of plaster, cork, cardboard or other material which covers the crown opening.

Pierced Ears: Little holes through the doll's earlobes to accommodate earrings.

Pierced-in Ears: A hole at the doll's earlobe which goes into the head to accommodate earrings.

Pink Bisque: A later bisque of about 1920 which was pre-colored pink.

Pink-toned China: China which has been given a pink tint to look more like real flesh color; also called lustered china.

Rembrandt Hair: Hair style parted in center with bangs at front, straight down sides and back and curled at ends.

S.G.D.G.: Used on French dolls to indicate that the patent is registered "without guarantee of the government."

Shoulder Head: A doll's head and shoulders all in one piece.

Shoulder Plate: The actual shoulder portion sometimes molded in one with the head, sometimes a separate piece with a socket in which a head is inserted.

Socket Head: Head and neck which fit into an opening in the shoulder plate or the body.

Solid-dome Head: Head with no crown opening, could have painted hair or be covered by wig.

Stationary Eyes: Glass eyes which do not move or sleep.

Stone Bisque: Coarse white bisque of a lesser quality.

Toddler Body: Usually a chubby ball-jointed composition body with chunky, shorter thighs, and a diagonal hip joint; sometimes has curved instead of jointed arms; sometimes is of five pieces with straight chubby legs.

Topsy-Turvy: Doll with two heads, one usually concealed beneath a skirt.

Turned Shoulder Head: Head and shoulders are one piece, but the head is molded at an angle so that the doll is not looking straight ahead.

Vinyl: Soft plastic material used for making dolls after 1950s.

Watermelon Mouth: Closed line-type mouth curved up at each side in an impish expression.

Wax Over: A doll with head and/or limbs of papier-mâché or composition covered with a layer of wax to give a natural, lifelike finish.

Weighted Eyes: Eyes which can be made to sleep by means of a weight which is attached to the eyes.

Wire Eyes: Eyes which can be made to sleep by means of a wire which protrudes from doll's head.

Selected Bibliography

Anderton, Johana. *Twentieth Century Dolls*. North Kansas City, Missouri: Trojan Press, 1971.

_____. *More Twentieth Century Dolls*. North Kansas City, Missouri: Athena Publishing Co., 1974.

Angione, Genevieve. *All-Bisque & Half-Bisque Dolls*. Exton, Pennsylvania: Schiffer Publishing Ltd., 1969.

Borger, Mona. *Chinas, Dolls for Study and Admiration*. San Francisco: Borger Publications, 1983.

Cieslik, Jürgen and Marianne. *German Doll Encyclopedia 1800-1939*. Cumberland, Maryland: Hobby House Press, Inc., 1985.

Coleman, Dorothy S., Elizabeth Ann and Evelyn Jane. *The Collector's Book of Dolls' Clothes, Costumes in Miniature*. New York: Crown Publishers, Inc., 1975.

_____. *The Collector's Encyclopedia of Dolls*. New York: Crown Publishers, Inc., 1968.

_____. *The Collector's Encyclopedia of Dolls, Vol. II*. New York: Crown Publishers, Inc., 1986.

Foulke, Jan. *Blue Book of Dolls & Values, Vol. I-VII*. Cumberland, Maryland: Hobby House Press, Inc., 1974-1986.

_____. *Doll Classics*. Cumberland, Maryland: Hobby House Press, Inc., 1987.

_____. *Focusing on Effanbee Composition Dolls*. Riverdale, Maryland: Hobby House Press, 1978.

_____. *Kestner, King of Dollmakers*. Cumberland, Maryland: Hobby House Press, Inc., 1982.

_____. *Simon & Halbig Dolls, The Artful Aspect*. Cumberland, Maryland: Hobby House Press, Inc., 1984.

_____. *Treasury of Madame Alexander Dolls*. Riverdale, Maryland: Hobby House Press, 1979.

Hillier, Mary. *Dolls and Doll Makers*. New York: G. P. Putnam's Sons, 1968.

King, Constance Eileen. *The Collector's History of Dolls*. London: Robert Hale, 1977; New York: St. Martin's Press, 1978.

Merrill, Madeline O. *The Art of Dolls 1700-1940*. Cumberland, Maryland: Hobby House Press, Inc., 1985.

Noble, John. *A Treasury of Beautiful Dolls*. New York: Hawthorn Books, 1971.

Shoemaker, Rhoda. *Compo Dolls, Cute and Collectible*. Menlo Park, California: 1971.

_____. *Compo Dolls, Cute and Collectible, Vol. II*. Menlo Park, California: 1973.

_____. *Compo Dolls, Cute and Collectible, Vol. III*. Menlo Park, California: 1979.

About the Author

The name Jan Foulke is synonymous with accurate information. As the author of the *Blue Book of Dolls & Values®*, she is the most quoted source on doll information and the most respected and recognized authority on dolls and doll prices in the world.

Born in Burlington, New Jersey, Jan Foulke has always had a fondness for dolls. She recalls, "Many happy hours of my childhood were spent with dolls as companions, since we lived on a quiet country road, and until I was ten, I was an only child." Jan received a B.A. from Columbia Union College, where she was named to the *Who's Who in American Colleges & Universities* and was graduated with high honors. Jan taught for twelve years, in the Montgomery County school system in Maryland and also supervised student teachers in English for the University of Maryland, where she did graduate work.

Jan and her husband, Howard, who photographs the dolls presented in the *Blue Book*, were both fond of antiquing as a hobby, and in 1972 they decided to open a small antique shop of their own. The interest of their daughter, Beth, in dolls sparked their curiosity about the history of old dolls — an interest that quite naturally grew out of their love of heirlooms. The stock in their antique shop gradually changed and evolved into an antique doll shop.

Early in the development of their antique doll shop, Jan and Howard realized that there was a critical need for an accurate and reliable doll identification and price guide resource. In the early 1970's, the Foulkes teamed up with Hobby House Press (publishers of *Doll Reader* Magazine) to produce (along with Thelma Bateman) the first *Blue Book of Dolls & Values*, originally published in 1974. Since that time, the Foulkes have exclusively authored and illustrated the seven successive editions, and today the *Blue Book* is regarded by collectors and dealers as the definitive source for doll prices and values.

Jan and Howard Foulke now dedicate all of their professional time to the world of dolls, writing and illustrating books and articles, appraising collections, lecturing on antique dolls, acting as consultants to museums, auction houses and major collectors, and buying and selling dolls both by mail order and through exhibits at major shows throughout the United States. Mrs. Foulke is a member of the United Federation of Doll Clubs, Doll Collectors of America, and the International Doll Academy.

Mrs. Foulke has appeared on numerous TV talk shows and is often quoted in newspaper and magazine articles as the ultimate source for doll pricing and trends in collecting. In 1985, both "USA Today" and "The Washington Post" observed that the *Blue Book of Dolls & Values* was "the bible of doll collecting."

In addition to her work on the eight editions of the *Blue Book of Dolls & Values*, Jan Foulke has also authored: *Focusing on Effanbee Composition Dolls; A Treasury of Madame Alexander Dolls; Kestner, King of Dollmakers; Simon & Halbig: The Artful Aspect; Focusing on Gebruder Heubach Dolls;* and *Doll Classics.*

Index

Text references are indicated in alphabetical and numerical order. Often there is a photograph to accompany the text reference. References to illustrations indicate that photographs appear on a different page.

Mold and Mark Numbers